INTERNATIONALLY ABREAST
EXERCISE AS MEDICINE

Inspiration, hope and courage through 25 years of breast
cancer dragon boat paddling.

Michelle Hanton OAM
&
Eleanor Nielsen

© Michelle Hanton OAM & Eleanor Nielsen

ISBN: 978-0-6452889-0-2

First Published October 2021

Published by Dragon Sisters

Cover & Interior Design by Debbie Hunter, Two Dogs Graphics and Design

Back Cover Image courtesy Kim Bonomo, *Save Our Sisters,* Miami, Florida, USA

ACKNOWLEDGEMENT

Internationally Abreast – Exercise as Medicine has been made possible thanks to Angel Investors who believed in and supported the mission to bring this publication to life.

Charles A Dixon

Jane Frost

Martine Paterson of MoodFoodRadio.com

Elspeth Humphries

Penny LaSette

Judy Smith

DEDICATIONS

Dedicated to the 24 courageous women who took the first bold steps in 1996 and paved the way for the global movement that inspired this book.

Abreast In A Boat 1996 Team Roster

1. Maria Always
2. Grace Barber
3. Sheila Blair*
4. Judy Caldwell
5. Pat Cryder
6. Carol Dale - still paddling
7. Jaqueline Davis
8. Kate Doyle
9. Shannon Dyakowska*
10. Jane Frost - still paddling
11. Reni Gitshmann
12. Susan Harris
13. Norma Hicks*
14. Brenda Hochachka
15. Gail Konantz*
16. Gladie Lindgren
17. Angie MacDougall
18. Esther Matsubuchi - still paddling
19. Deb Middleton - still paddling
20. Coro Mohr
21. Sandra Morris
22. Diane Peain
23. Lucy Phua
24. Edith Templeton

*Deceased

FOREWORD

Forty feet long and weighing 500 pounds, a dragon boat is solid, stable and colorful, particularly when fitted with a dragon head and tail. It has 2000 years of history and sitting in the water it can appear intimidating. To breast cancer paddlers, it is an old friend. This vessel holds memories of laughter, fatigue, togetherness, teamwork, trust and love. From the beginning, the only criteria for inclusion in this boat was the diagnosis of breast cancer, which creates an immediate bond- 'all in the same boat' has never been more valid.

Paddling a dragon boat is not easy, but neither is treatment and recovery from breast cancer. Twenty paddlers, a steersperson and a drummer must act in unison; indeed, 22 people must think and act as one. As an individual paddler you are anonymous, protected by others all striving to look and perform the same. When the 20 paddles connect together, it is synchronicity; suddenly, the boat picks up and moves quickly over the water, racing effortlessly with only the sound of the paddle establishing a rapid pace. There is no fatigue, just wonder and joy- you could paddle forever.

The first year was all about lymphedema. Competition was never on the radar; making it to the start line was the real goal. Twenty-four incredibly courageous women were dedicated to showing that vigorous, repetitive upper body exercise would not result in breast cancer-related lymphedema. Proving that hypothesis would empower thousands of women to push the reset button and enjoy full and active lives.

From the start, Michelle Hanton and Eleanor Nielsen were on the front line and provided the leadership to nurture this program to success in two continents. This is a story that merits telling. They have assembled a group of individuals who have experienced, been touched by or contributed to this narrative. Eleanor and Michelle are part of a very special group of women, scattered throughout the world, who have worked hard, selflessly, so that this program would evolve. Collectively they had the passion, perseverance, and a sense of purpose to make this a global success. Their commitment to other women with the devastating diagnosis of breast cancer is legend, and the kindness and support that their teams provide exemplify the best of humanity.

With respect and admiration,

Don McKenzie
15/08/2021

INTRODUCTION

The flotilla of breast cancer survivors provides a beacon of hope in a dark, long, and lonely tunnel, which takes many twists and turns. A tunnel filled with fear. The smell of hospitals, of chemotherapy drugs. Oncologists. Surgeons.

A glimmer of light. A flicker of hope. A flash of pink amongst the ocean of fear. Dragon boat paddling is an unlikely silver lining on the journey with breast cancer. For many, it is the start of an incredible journey to freedom and empowerment.

Freedom from limiting beliefs that you will never be whole again. Freedom to discover the joy of exercise. Empowered to live life to the full after being confronted with your mortality. Confident to be in the moment.

It is also a journey of opportunity that opens up a whole new world. A journey that brings amazing friendships, many of which are unlikely. Friendships that would never have occurred if not for breast cancer and the dragon boat.

One such friendship is the one that developed between us and brought forth the idea for this book. If not for breast cancer, we would never have met—an age gap of some 20 years means little when you share the dragon spirit.

We are blessed to be able to call ourselves 'thrivers' post breast cancer diagnosis. Just as the world of breast cancer treatment has evolved and changed, so too has the breast cancer paddler movement.

Our history is what shapes the future. As the world around us changes, it is easy to forget our collective past. Yet remembering our roots and, more importantly, the reason we fanned the flames of the dragon spirit across the world is paramount. If we lose sight of our why, we simply become another dragon boat team.

Our collective past is filled with great positivity, exerting a profound impact on those who continue to be newly diagnosed with this insidious disease. In writing this book, we sought out members who had more recently joined a team. We were curious to learn, based on the fact that there is more open awareness of breast cancer within communities, if the fear of being diagnosed has reduced over the past 25 years.

The feedback indicates that despite the advances in medical treatment and publicity surrounding breast cancer awareness, a massive cloud of fear still exists amongst those newly diagnosed. The need for the breast cancer dragon boat program remains as strong today as it was 25 years ago.

Within these pages, we aimed to capture the foundation built over the past 25 years by those living with breast cancer who choose to embrace the dragon spirit.

The difficulty in collating a complete picture of what has transpired globally has been an enormous challenge. At times, we have felt our names should have been Holmes and Watson. Despite our best efforts, we cannot guarantee the information is 100% accurate in every detail; experience lies very much in the minds and memories of individuals.

Internationally Abreast – Exercise as Medicine is a story of hope and courage. It is about living with breast cancer and believing in the unwavering power to make a difference to those who follow us down this pathway. We may not have chosen this path for ourselves but are blessed to walk it surrounded by the embrace of a global flotilla that keeps the spirit alive.

Eleanor Nielsen & Michelle Hanton OAM

ABOUT DRAGON BOAT RACING

Dragon boating, steeped in ancient culture and traditions dating back over 2000 years, began in southern China. It was listed as a National/UNESCO Intangible Cultural Heritage Item and selected initially into the National Intangible Cultural Heritage on 20 May 2006. The Dragon Boat Festival was, on 30 October 2009, added to the UNESCO Representative List of the Intangible Cultural Heritage of Humanity.

Chinese festivals are based on the agricultural cycle. Dragon boat races were held to avert misfortune and encourage the rains needed for prosperity. The object of worship was the dragon—the most venerated of the Chinese zodiac deities and traditionally a symbol of water. The dragon is believed to rule the rivers, seas, and dominate the weather.

A highly visual dimension to dragon boating traditions is the legend of a beloved Chinese poet and popular statesman—Qu Yuan, who lived in Hunan Province over 2000 years ago. Although there are several versions of the legend, all agree that Qu Yuan drowned himself in the Mi Lo River, distraught at falling from grace. The local fishermen rushed out in their boats to save him. Thrashing the water with their paddles, beating drums, and throwing rice dumplings into the river to appease the water spirits and ensure the fish did not eat his body.

The death of Qu Yuan is commemorated every year by the Chinese with a dragon boat festival held on the fifth day of the fifth lunar month (between the end of May and the end of June). The beginnings of dragon boat racing are credited to the legend of Qu Yuan.

These traditions and legends make the sport vibrant and spectacular from both the participant and spectator perspectives.

'The diagnosis was a surprise to me, but I really should have seen the signs which were present. I was just too distracted by work and did not have enough respect for my body, trying to tell me something was wrong. Also, when the mammogram came back negative, I just accepted the result. In retrospect, I should have insisted on a follow-up and ultrasound when I noticed the nipple changes.

I remember a little voice in my head spoke to me. It was serene and managed to quiet all other thoughts in my head. It said, 'Yes, it is cancerous, and no, it will not kill you.'

That voice only spoke to me one more time during my journey. At the end, and being very grateful that I had survived, I asked myself how I should give back. And the voice said, 'Live.' It solidified for me that the best way I can appreciate the life that I have been given back is to live it fully and embrace all that life has to offer.'

Akaash Singh, *Dragons Abreast Toronto*

DRAGON BOAT TRADITIONS

It is traditional for dragon boats to receive a blessing before taking to the water for the first time and ensuring good karma for the races and paddlers. It is considered bad luck not to have a boat traditionally blessed before putting it on the water

The Third Eye, located in the centre of the forehead, is the wisdom eye. Opening the third eye gives the dragon (ergo, the team) clarity and focus. Painting a red line down the centre of the forehead opens the third eye. The other eyes are also traditionally dotted at the beginning of each Festival—ensuring the dragon can see clearly and far. This task is considered an honour, and dignitaries are often asked to perform the role as a mark of respect.

Buddhist monks have traditionally performed a ceremony involving chanting—asking the spirits to watch over and bless the competitors, ensuring no harm befalls them. Permission is requested to allow the Hungry Ghosts mouths to open to eat the offerings. During the chanting, a bell rings, or a traditional Tibetan bowl sounds. The sound awakens the water spirits, letting them know the boat is coming into their territory. It is considered extremely bad form for a boat to enter the water without first seeking permission from the spirits. Rice dumplings—parcels of rice wrapped in banana leaf—are tossed into the water as an offering to the water spirits ensuring they protect the paddlers and do not rock the boat.

Depending on the format followed, you will sometimes find the monks tie blessing bands on each paddler at the end of the blessing ceremony. These bands are considered lucky charms and should not be cut off but worn until they fall off naturally.

In more recent times, blessing ceremonies have included Hindu and Christian blessings in conjunction with or alternative to the traditional Buddhist tradition. Boats are also blessed before the beginning of each dragon boat season and at many major regattas.

The drums always sound during races ensuring that the water spirits know that the dragon boat is coming. Traditionally the rhythmic beat of the drum serves to sound out commands to the paddlers to increase or decrease the stroke rate. Western counterparts very much admire the highly skilled drummers in Asian countries. In most western countries, crews use an electronic communication speaker system to relay commands through the boat.

The doctors may have saved our lives, but it is the sport of dragon boating that has saved our spirit.

Kim Bonomo, *Save Our Sisters*, Miami, USA

DRAGON BOAT As A Modern Sport

The Hong Kong Tourist Association recognised the tourism drawcard of dragon boat racing. In 1976, it hosted the first international dragon boat race as a modern competitive sports event in conjunction with the Association of Hong Kong Fishermen.

Today, you will find dragon boats across the globe. Races vary from local community festivals and friendly corporate regattas right through to highly competitive national and international competitions culminating in the World Championships hosted by the International Dragon Boat Federation (IDBF), the peak body for the sport.

The IDBF estimates that worldwide, over 50 million people participate in dragon boat racing annually, with the majority from China and nearby Asian neighbours.

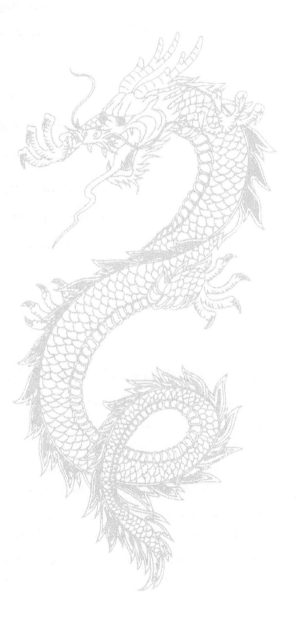

DRAGON BOAT And Breast Cancer

The popularity and growth of the sport amongst those diagnosed with breast cancer comes down to the fact that it is an empowering positive experience on so many different levels.

Sporting abilities are not a requirement because you are literally all in the same boat. Unlike other physical team activities where, if you stop, you are left behind, in the dragon boat when you get tired, you are still carried forward with the team.

The global focus of the movement is on helping individuals regain full and active lives after a breast cancer diagnosis whilst raising awareness of the disease in their local communities.

Shock. Anger. Depression

Loss of personal control

Disfigurement from surgery

Loss of fitness and flexibility

Lymphatic system compromised

Chemotherapy – radiotherapy

Medical Merry Go Round – stops!

It's time to get off and get on with your life.

Treatment is over. Off you go.

But where?

IF YOU ARE READING THIS TODAY,
THE ANSWER FOR MANY IS THE DRAGON BOAT.

In the ancient city of Venice, sitting alongside the Grand Canal sipping an aperitif, it is not uncommon for a dragon boat filled with women clad in pink to come paddling past.

In Florence, walking alongside the Arno, you will spot a similar scene. A flotilla of women dressed in pink, chattering loudly and excitedly. The same picture repeats on waterways across the globe.

The languages may be different, yet the laughing, chattering and banter is always the same. The one common thread that binds these pink-clad groups of individuals together is the BIG C. Yes, cancer. More precisely, breast cancer.

Cancer is a word that sends terrors into the hearts of those diagnosed. Yet, amongst each of these groups congregated together in pink is incredible joie de vivre. Grasping the paddle firmly between both hands, the magic combination of the dragon boat and breast cancer binds participants together.

HOW IT BEGAN.

It began with a softly spoken, humble and remarkable man .

Dr Don McKenzie is a household name today synonymous with dragon boat and breast cancer. Dr Don, as his fans often refer to him. (You read that right; he has an unofficial fan club, made up mainly of women over 45 who believe he is a superhero). He gave us the gift of the dragon boat—the light at the end of a very dark treatment tunnel.

In 1996, Dr Don McKenzie, a sports medicine specialist at the University of British Columbia (UBC), Canada, had a patient advised to avoid exercise, especially repetitive upper body arm movements. When exploring why that advice was given, the patient explained she had undergone surgery for breast cancer. In those days, it was common to tell patients not to engage in strenuous and repetitive upper body exercises post-surgical node dissection and radiation therapy.

The reason? Fear of developing lymphedema. Lymphedema is a poorly understood and disabling side effect that results in a swollen arm. It often occurs in those with lymph nodes removed as a part of their breast cancer surgery. Removing lymph nodes from the axilla (armpit) at the time of a lumpectomy or mastectomy was common practice.

Thanks to advances in medical science, breast surgery has changed over the last 26 years. Axillary clearance is not as common today. But back in 1996, it was standard procedure. The fear of developing lymphedema was terrifying.

As a sports medicine physician and researcher, questioning the logic behind activity restrictions came naturally to Dr Don. Being a canoeist himself, he knew first-hand the type of movement involved. He felt that surely there could only be benefits from being out on the water and doing upper body exercise to strengthen muscles affected by cancer treatments. He immediately thought of the dragon boat as the perfect vehicle for a clinical study.

Introduced to Canada in 1986, dragon boating was still predominantly an all-male sport ten years later in 1996. There were only a few mixed teams, with the official ratio, at that time, being 5 women and 17 men.

Recruiting 24 women, strangers to each other, ranging in age from 32 to 64 years young, the number needed to form a dragon boat crew, Dr Don McKenzie's research study was ready to begin. Carefully monitored, they trained for six months with the end goal being to debut the team at the annual International Alcan Festival, held each June on False Creek, Vancouver.

Spectators and officials were accustomed to seeing strapping young men race down the course. The sight of 24 women, all ages and sizes dressed in fuschia pink was a shock! The crowds went wild, clapping and cheering as the fuschia boat crossed the finish line.

Carol Dale recalls how she signed up, 'No time trials; no resumes, no interviews. We just responded to a call for volunteers to begin a program of dragon boat racing that would test the current protocols around the limitations of upper body exercise after surgery for breast cancer.

The call went out to support groups and organisations focused on breast cancer recovery issues across the lower mainland surrounding Vancouver, British Columbia, Canada. It was to be a six-month study.

We gathered in a meeting room at the Sports Medicine Centre, University of British Columbia in January 1996, twenty-four of us, curious to learn what was ahead. Little did we know what that six-month experiment would produce.'

Jane Frost, another of the original women who signed up and is, today, a familiar name to many in breast cancer paddling, shares, 'Don was cautious and careful with us, making us wear compression sleeves and measuring our arms before and after every practice.

He sent us all to the gym for three months, something many of us had never done before. The first time we paddled together, we were on the water for an hour and a half. We paddled for 14 minutes.'

Of her fellow teammates, Carol recalls, 'We were indeed diverse: Lucy, a Philippine nanny, age 32; Jackie, a First Nations woman who started a support group for aboriginal women; Esther, a Japanese-Canadian who had been interned during WWII and had a large and supportive family who cheered us on at every opportunity; indeed many families followed our every move. Were they concerned for our safety? Perhaps at first. However, as the season progressed, they were proud of what we were accomplishing. As were we! We had gone from scared to brave almost overnight. We raced against mixed crews at the International Dragon Boat Festival in Vancouver that June, over a course that was 645 metres. We were *first in our lane* and knew, at that moment, that other women simply had to be offered this experience. A six-month experiment has become a 25-year phenomenon.'

When the boat paddled back to shore, an archway of cheering spectators formed as the team disembarked. Beaming, delighted family members gazed on in awe of their previously weak and ill mother, sister, wife responding so enthusiastically to this new experience.

Dr Don McKenzie's goal of changing accepted practice following breast cancer surgery had begun. The key difference between *Abreast In A Boat* and the other teams on the waters of False Creek that day was that instead of focusing on winning the race, their goal was to finish the race. We finished *first in our lane!* is a phrase you will frequently hear from those who embrace the dragon spirit instilled by Dr Don McKenzie and *Abreast In A Boat*.

On that historic day, back in 1996, steps were taken to raise awareness of breast cancer as a common risk to women of all ages and men. Kate Doyle, a social worker, was on the team and noticed that the group had evolved from complete strangers to a bonded group of women in three short months. The phenomenon was worth documenting.

'We could not say yes fast enough,' is Jane Frost's recollection of the team reaction to being asked to participate in a study about the impact paddling had on their lives.

'We were to consider what paddling meant to us, to our family and friends. Had it made a difference to our lives, and if so, in what way? Had we learned things about ourselves through our paddling? What did we see had changed for ourselves?' When the paper was published, it was a clear endorsement of the remarkable experience the team had undergone.

Esther Matsubuchi, another of the 24 original paddlers, shares 'I cannot believe that a quarter-century has passed since I first sat down in a dragon boat. Who would have thought that a couple of dozen breast cancer survivors attending Vancouver-area support groups could be enticed to start dragon boating for research, let alone for fun?

Before our first season in 1996, all strenuous, repetitive upper body movements were discouraged. Even knitting, playing the piano, and gardening was discouraged. Tending to rose bushes was a no-no for fear that a thorn could prick a finger and lead to infection and lymphedema.

My whole life, I was interested in dragon boats. However, I never dreamed that I would ever have the chance to paddle, let alone competitively. The closest I came to the water was hearing my neighbour telling me about her daughter's dragon boat experience: paddling was hard, and the team was wet and cold each time they got on the water.

Everything changed in 1996 when a couple of women from the University of British Columbia visited my breast cancer support group and told us about their proposed study involving breast cancer and lymphedema. They were trying to recruit breast cancer survivors who would volunteer to join a dragon boat team for a season. We were being asked to take a chance and see if vigorous cardio and repetitive upper body movement really did cause lymphedema. I did not volunteer right away, but when I saw another woman raise her hand, I raised my hand, too. I didn't care about this being a study by physiotherapists working on their doctorate degrees. It was my chance to be a dragon boater! In the end, that other woman did not paddle, but for me, the rest is history.

That first day, I remember climbing over three boats to get to our assigned boat. We paddled to the start line. I was so tired and I told myself, 'This is the last race I'll be paddling in.' We made it to the finish line, out of breath but completely exhilarated. I don't remember if this phrase started here that day, but we were *first in our lane*—unless we were second in someone else. We still hear that phrase to this day.'

When the team told Dr Don his six-month project had a good deal longer lifespan than he had envisioned at the outset he did not hesitate for one moment to support the initiative.

Abreast In A Boat's goal after that first year was to work with novices, people treated for breast cancer. Ready to lead them into another world where they would find fitness, camaraderie, support and friendship from a group of people who had shared similar experiences. They were also determined to spread their message around the world.

We all could see it was not the paddling that had created this phenomenon; the paddling had given us the vessel we could use to regain control of our lives.

Jane Frost, *Abreast In A Boat*,
Vancouver, Canada

I was diagnosed in 2018, at the age of 47.

It was three weeks between my doctor saying he needed to see me and the diagnosis. I had flown to Ireland as my father was dying, and during this time, I kept thinking it's not good news. I had my suspicions. I was shocked and scared. My family doctor wanted to talk to me in person because of family history: I had a sister pass away 21 years prior of breast cancer.

I was more worried about my wife, and 'how we were going to get through this, and how am I gonna tell my friends and family. What if I die?

Geraldine Brady, *Dragons Abreast Toronto*

THE FLOWER CEREMONY

Like many of the beautiful happenings in the world of breast cancer paddling, the powerfully moving Flower Ceremony synonymous with remembrance came about because one person had an idea.

Brenda Hochachka, from *Abreast In A Boat* recalls, 'Before leaving at dawn for our inaugural race, I noticed that a 20-year-old climbing rose in my garden was at its prime with small fuchsia flowers. Enough for one each for every paddler on our boat. These flowers enhanced the team headbands, and each was worn differently.

The tough little blooms survived two days of paddling, but what to do with them after the last race? As the boat pulled towards the dock, there was a pause in the paddling. The flowers were tossed into the waters of False Creek in remembrance of those women we knew who had not survived breast cancer or were too sick to paddle.

We were feeling grateful to have had such an exciting weekend. In fact, a wonderful spring getting to know each other and learning paddling skills from our coaches, culminating in the regatta.'

The following year, *Abreast In A Boat* increased to three teams and participated in the world's first breast cancer race. Dorothy Cichecki, a novice paddler, could not participate due to treatment for a recurrence but was certainly in the boat in spirit. Teammate, Jeanne Stiles, arranged for Dorothy's headband to be tied to the dragon boat and crew members to carry a pink carnation as a token of their hopes and prayers for Dorothy's recovery.

At the end of the race, the crew tossed their flowers into the water in a spontaneous moment. This was the first time flowers were thrown after a breast cancer race.

By 1998, breast cancer teams had grown—survivor races took place in Vancouver, Montreal, and Toronto. In all three cities, ahead of the final breast cancer race, paddlers of the participating crews had decided to link boats, have flowers ready, and toss the flowers into the water after a moment of silence. These were the first officially organised Flower Ceremonies.

In subsequent years the ceremony has become more elaborate but no less moving.

Regatta proceedings halt. Sometimes a song is sung as the shore crowds share the unique and poignant occasion.

Brenda, who is still paddling, shares, 'The original rose bush thrives still. It is a reminder even after 27 years since that first regatta of an emotional and spontaneous catharsis of remembrance and gratitude for health and fitness.'

There is nothing more moving in our sport than the sight of the breast cancer survivor paddling crews gathering on the water after the finish of their last race.

There they sit in their boats, scattering pink petals on the water around them, in memory of those who have lost their fight for life.

It always brings a tear to my eyes and a moment of quiet reflection too.

Mike Haslam, IDBF Founder & Honourary President

THE DRAGONS SHAKE THEIR HEADS

The dragons shake their heads in wonderment.
This was not the way it was meant to be.
They were born to carry the strong, the sinews of steel;
They were born to carry the warriors, the men in their vigour;
They were born to carry the fierce paddlers on to victory;
They were born to carry only the bravest and the best.

THE DRAGONS SHAKE THEIR HEADS

Who are this new breed of paddlers?
They are not fit; they are not strong;
They come not from warrior stock;
They bring neither hardened muscle nor tempered sinews.
They are women, deeply wounded in body and soul,
And bring with them only determination and hope.
How can these be victors?

THE DRAGONS SHAKE THEIR HEADS

They have no depth of skill, no reserves of stamina.
They tire; they flag; they droop exhausted
When the long, long pull is finished.
They lack the rhythm; they lack the deep, deep drive;
They gasp and are hollow-eyes at the end of practice.
They have only determination and hope.
How can these be victors?

THE DRAGONS SHAKE THEIR HEADS

They have joined their hands and their hearts.
They have danced and waved their paddles on high.
These pink-clad women warriors have shown the dragon boats
from many lands
That they can pull, that they can race,
That they can survive.

They are saluted by each and every other crew.
Because, above all else, they have determination and hope.
Because, above all else, they can be victors.
Because, above all else, they are the bravest and the best.
The dragons nod their heads in praise and wonderment.

Danny Daniels, June 1999, husband of Marjorie Daniels, a team member of *Island Breaststrokes*

I used to visualise my tumour in the water, and with each stroke, I took I would bash the hell out of my cancer.

Little did I know that it would quell my angst. I firmly believe that my association with dragon boat racing for the last 24 years has kept me mentally, spiritually, and physically alive.

Irene Brooksbank, *Dragons Abreast Toronto*

Toronto, Canada's largest city, was the second city in Canada to establish a breast cancer team after Eleanor Nielsen, a nurse by profession, met some of the *Originals* from *Abreast In A Boat* at a breast cancer conference in Vancouver in 1996.

Eleanor's diagnosis in 1989 was no surprise as she had a family history of breast cancer. 'My aunt had just died, followed by my uncle. As a nurse, I had seen mostly the worst of breast cancer in hospitals. I knew no one who had survived and feared the worst with no children's weddings, no grandchildren, a short lifetime and the end of many dreams. I still remember the relief when the nurse removing my stitches told me it had been 10 years since she had breast cancer surgery.

My fears were typical of so many who never saw women living with breast cancer, and only knew of dying. One of the greatest gifts the breast cancer dragon boat community has given the world is a vivid and joyous picture of women living life to the fullest after breast cancer.'

Eleanor recalls meeting *Abreast In A Boat*, 'I was very impressed by their enthusiasm and excitement for dragon boating. I went home, thinking if Vancouver has enough women with breast cancer to do this, Toronto surely must have more.' Egged on by her husband Charles, who simply said 'Go for it,' Eleanor began recruiting interested women. 'When I embarked on starting the team, I was in a state of ignorant bliss. I didn't even know what a dragon boat looked like.'

A fellow breast cancer survivor working at Mount Sinai Hospital, Rose Jones paddled with the hospital dragon boat team participating in the annual dragon boat festival organised by the Toronto Chinese Business Association each June. In November 1997, Eleanor and Rose pulled together the first team of breast cancer survivors in Ontario. Winter training started in the pool, where they were taught the A-frame and positioning for paddling.

'We were naive in the extreme and at the first Festival, ran into trouble by wearing race shirts with a large sponsor name on them. It turned out this wasn't allowed. Toronto was using the original teak dragon boats at that time—super heavy, and the race length was 640 metres. It was definitely a workout!'

Meanwhile, in Quebec, the first survivor team, *Two Abreast / Côte-à-côte*, founded by Robin Hornstein launched in Montreal on 14 December 1997.

In 1999, *Abreast In A Boat* held a conference for breast cancer teams across Canada. The event was two days of talks and discussions on common issues, followed by the ALCAN International Dragon Boat Festival at False Creek.

Ten teams attended; from Victoria to Halifax and *Pink Phoenix*, from Portland, Oregon. *Prairie Partners* was a landmark first for Canada, a composite of several prairie teams who could not field entire crews for the Festival.

Over the two days, it quickly became apparent that any problems facing one team reflected the same issues for other groups. Topics under discussion were Team Dynamics, more aptly called Shut Up and Paddle, Media Relations, Sponsor Relations, Dragon Boat Training, and Coping with Recurrence and Loss.

The Conference was such a joyful experience that a decision was made for Toronto to host the next Conference in 2001.

By the time *Dragons Abreast Toronto* hosted the 2001 Conference¬— thanks to financial support from the Canadian Breast Cancer Foundation and Scotiabank, the survivor paddler movement numbers had grown. The The Conference coincided with the annual Toronto International Dragon Boat Race Festival in June 2001. Teams attending were *Breast Friends,* Edmonton; *Chemo Savvy,* Winnipeg; *Sistership,* Calgary; *Survivors Abreast,* Peterborough; *Survivor Thrivers,* Cobourg; *Warriors of Hope,* North Bay; *Hope Chest,* Buffalo, USA; and a combined team from Brandon, London, Toronto, Vancouver and Australia. This team was named *Internationally Abreast,* modelled after *Prairie Partners* from 1999.

Similar in format to the Vancouver conference, there was a strong focus on team dynamics. Reporting on common team problems, one of the speakers, a sports psychologist, mentioned that most team members participate for fun, social interaction, fitness and health. A smaller percentage focused on achievement. The other challenge was dealing with the pain of diagnosis of recurrence, metastatic spread, and team members' death.

The broad consensus in 2001 and today, 20 years later, is that focusing on what brought the team together is paramount. Losing sight of our origins makes us simply another dragon boat team. The only criteria to joining one of the breast cancer teams are to have been diagnosed with breast cancer. This is what makes our teams unique, giving us the privilege of raising awareness of breast cancer and demonstrating the benefits of living a full and active life after diagnosis and treatment. It changes the public perception of breast cancer from one of fear to one of hope.

In 2021, there are approximately 53 breast cancer paddling teams in Canada.

'Stepping into a dragon boat at the age of 71 began a new and challenging activity for me. Never in my wildest dreams did I expect, at age 93, to be continuing to enjoy the sport.'

Nina Burgess, *Dragons Abreast Toronto*

DRAGONS ABREAST TORONTO TEAM SONG

Dragons Abreast are we
Paddling together
Pulling and gliding while
Keeping the pace
Reach out, this boat can fly
We're going to touch the sky.

Pounding of dragon hearts
Say, can you hear them?
Stroking to drummer's beat
We'll never stop.
Wild women strong and free
Dragons Abreast are we.

Pacers are digging deep
Feeling the power
Hearts of the Engine room
Beating as one.
Boosts from the Rockets blast
Damned if we will be last!

Keeping the hope alive
Raising awareness
Heeding the warrior's cry
Find us the cure.
Paddling from sea to sea
Onward to victory.

Boom di dyada, boom di dyada,
Boom di dyada, boom,boom,boom

Carol Pigott, *Dragons Abreast Toronto*

Pagayer seule c'est bien, mais pagayer a deux, côtes-à-côtes c'est mieux

(translation : paddling alone is nice, but paddling side-by-side, is better)

Gisella Casati, *Two Abreast /Côte-à-côte*

TWO ABREAST -
CÔTE-À-CÔTE,
TEAM SONG

Two Abreast is who we are
Bringing women near and far
With bodies strong and dragon's might
Two Abreast is here to fight
There's hope and laughter in our song
Hear our voices loud and strong
Celebrating life for sure
Célébrons la vie, Côte-à-côte, c'est nous !

Portland, Oregon, is home to *Pink Phoenix*, the first breast cancer dragon boat team in the USA. It was founded in 1997 by breast cancer survivor Web Eberhart and her good friend Dorothy Atwood, a dragon boat paddler.

They had dreamed about starting a team for a year based on Dorothy's experience and Web's love of a breast cancer group of ballet dancers. Dorothy encountered *Abreast In A Boat* in 1996 in Vancouver while paddling with another team. She went home fired up to start a team in Portland. Web had said about her ballet group, 'It was really powerful to do something physical with your body in a group of other women with breast cancer.'

The name *Pink Phoenix* represents arising from the ashes—an apt way of describing breast cancer paddlers.

Dorothy set about recruiting with the help of the Susan G Komen Foundation, writing letters to all breast cancer survivor participants in the 1996 Race for the Cure. The first team to hit the water as *Pink Phoenix* in 1997 ranged from age 29 to mid-60 and included Michele Gorman, who became the team captain.

The Gorman Cup is an exhibition dragon boat race during the lunch break on the first day of the Portland Rose Festival Dragon Boat races. Named after and honouring the memory of Michele Gorman, founding captain of *Pink Phoenix*, who lost her battle with breast cancer in the spring of 1998. All breast cancer survivors, paddling and non paddling are invited to participate. The only requirement is being able to get in and out of the boat.

Fran Breiling, a mother of 6, grandmother of 10 and member for the last 19 years, shares the memory of her first Rose Festival in 2002, 'Our team had four boats, one being a select or competitive boat. The boats were very heavy, and we pretty much paddled only on one side. It was a struggle to get through those races, but we felt more empowered and stronger afterwards. Husbands of our members greeted us with roses at the top of the stairs before the paddle arch.'

The Portland Dragon Boat Rose Festival hosted by the Portland-Kaohsiung, Sister City Association, is a cultural event held annually in June. All races take place in boats traditionally used in Kaohsiung, Taiwan. These are more stable, wider, and heavier than the dragon boats familiar to most crews.

A unique feature of this race is that each crew also needs a flag catcher besides having steer, paddlers, and a drummer. The flag catcher needs nerves of steel, as their role involves crawling up the neck onto the dragon's head. At the same time, the racing boat is in full motion —lying between the horns whilst reaching as far forward as they dare to catch the flag sitting on top of the buoy at the finish line! The race time allocated hinges on catching the flag.

Fran sums up her 19 years with *Pink Phoenix* 'The biggest blessing is the friendships and individual comradery between team members and the sense of physical empowerment. This was a gift from breast cancer, a road I never dreamed I would take.'

'It's not about you being the fastest or the strongest. It's about, we are in it together,' is how Meg Kilmer describes what it means to be a breast cancer survivor paddler.

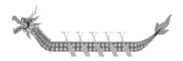

Buffalo, New York, the opposite side of the country to *Pink Phoenix* in Oregon, is home to the second breast cancer survivor team in the United States. Laurie Hyzy founded *Hope Chest*.

Laurie and Nina Sacco shared a close friendship and an interest in exercise, aspiring to become personal trainers. Despite a diagnosis of breast cancer, Nina exercised whenever possible. She was determined to make a difference in the lives of breast cancer survivors. This philosophy for encouraging breast cancer survivors to return to an unrestricted, active lifestyle became the foundation of *Hope Chest*.

Sadly, Nina lost her eight-year battle in May 2000, a few short months before *Hope Chest* participated in their first race. Nina's dream lives on; her spirit and influence are remembered in the name of their registered 501 (c)(3) not-for-profit agency Luminina which means 'Light of Nina'.

Anne Kist, joining the team in 2001, is the current program director coach at the time of writing this book. She shares, 'We are currently in our 21st year and continue to grow in number. There are over 125 active members, and when we hold our own Festival, we have three teams entered.'

Anne credits the membership numbers to the fact that *Hope Chest* offers free exercise and nutrition classes throughout the year, and 'practice for our dragon boating is from May through September. Although we have won only a few races in the past 21 years, we are always *first in our lane*. The support and camaraderie are second to none.'

In 2021, there are approximately 61 breast cancer teams in the USA.

' *You can't be a superstar and paddle the boat. You need 19 other people, and you have to be in sync.* '

Annette Johnson, *Pink Phoenix,*
Portland, USA

'WHAT DO YOU DO SURVIVING BREAST CANCER'

(*Hope Chest* Song sung to the tune of 'Drunken Sailor')

What do you do surviving breast cancer?
What do you do surviving breast cancer?
What do you do surviving breast cancer?
    Dragon boat racing

Hey, hey, up we're rising
Hey, hey, we're surviving
Hey, hey, watch us thriving
    Dragon boat racing

Get in a boat and start to paddle
Get in a boat and start to paddle
Get in a boat and start to paddle
    Dragon boat racing

Hey, hey, up we're rising
Hey, hey, we're surviving
Hey, hey, watch us thriving
    Dragon boat racing

Why would I do that with my sisters?
Why would I do that with my sisters?
Why would I do that with my sisters?
    Dragon boat racing

Hey, hey, up we're rising
Hey, hey, we're surviving
Hey, hey, watch us thriving
    Dragon boat racing

Cuz it's fun and we just love it
Cuz it's fun and we just love it
Cuz it's fun and we just love it
    Dragon boat racing

Hey, hey, up we're rising
Hey, hey, we're surviving
Hey, hey, watch us thriving
    Dragon boat racing

Making memories makes us stronger
Making memories makes us stronger
Making memories makes us stronger
    Dragon boat racing

Hey, hey, up we're rising
Hey, hey, we're surviving
Hey, hey, watch us thriving
    Dragon boat racing

One of my most vivid memories was how, six months after we began as a team, we found a way to get to Abreast in a Boat's first National Dragon boat festival in Vancouver 2009. With no money to bring the whole team across the country, the idea came for each Buddy to purchase their own paddle and have people sign the blade for a donation. Several people collected enough donations to completely pay for their trip.

But the very best part of this idea was that as we readied to put our paddles in the water for our first race ever, we each could read the names of all those who were supporting us. So they symbolically joined us to celebrate the most important race we had each already won. This memory still brings tears of joy and gratitude.

Sharon Driscoll, *Bosom Buddies*, Nova Scotia, Canada

'My first diagnosis was in 1992 and again in 1997. I first stepped into a dragon boat in 2012; I am proof that there is lots of good living despite my metastatic stage 4 breast cancer, diagnosed in 2011.

The dragon boat has allowed me to exercise, which is good for my bones and provides me with strength, power, and friendship. Carpe Diem!!'

Kerrie Dowding, *Dragons Abreast Penrith*, NSW, Australia

NEW ZEALAND

On the southern tip of the beautiful North Island in the land of the long white cloud lies Wellington. Renowned for the winds and turbulent seas that rush through the passage between the South Pacific and the Tasman Sea, Windy Wellington is an apt nickname.

Don McKenzie and Jane Frost spotted a poster advertising the 1998 World Club Championships while walking around the False Creek regatta site. Jane remembers, 'We wanted to spread the message about the benefits of exercise after diagnosis and treatment for breast cancer and the remarkable time we were having getting stronger. Right then and there, we decided *Abreast In A Boat* should attend.

One of the things we do when we go to new places is meet with sponsors. In Wellington, there was a branch office of our sponsor Colliers International. A few of us went to say thank you to them.

We were greeted by the managing partner who had rounded up some of his staff. The poor man was clearly confused because he told us there was no breast cancer in New Zealand so he wondered aloud why we came?

We smiled and departed, shaking our heads. The next day at the race site, two of the Colliers men appeared. When they saw each other, they confessed to us and each other that one's mother had breast cancer and the other's sister had it.'

Gail Konantz, paddling on this historic trip, described *Abreast In A Boat's* first time out on the water in Wellington.

'Busting with confidence, we headed out, under a bridge into a surging sea. Suddenly we were rolling and pitching. We stopped paddling, and over we went. Our first dump! It was a big surprise.

Once safely back in the lagoon, we were assured there was no need to dump. All we had to do was stabilise by putting our paddles flat to the water, and as they explained how easy it was to do, we dumped again!

With confidence levels at an all-time low, we assembled for our first race the next day. We were in danger of being this wimpy group of breast cancer survivors who came all the way from Canada just to dump in the bay.

Ready for our first race, equipped with our lumpy water skills, 'Stabilise or paddle like hell even if you're sinking', we lurched out to the start.

Each of us was dealing with her private terrors and fears, including discovering there were sharks in the harbour. We absolutely had to stay upright, and we had to finish.

The wind gusts were 45 to 60 kms per hour. We later heard the highest gusts were 100 km per hour, and after our race, the rest of the races for the day were cancelled.

While more than 40 boats dumped over the course of those three days, we never tipped again in any of our seven races.'

Media attention was overwhelming, including the front page cover of the national newspaper. 24 women who had travelled halfway around the world, practised for months in the freezing cold weather of a Vancouver winter floating in Wellington Harbour was definitely newsworthy and resulted in the establishment of *Busting With Life*, the first survivor team in New Zealand.

Trici Nelson, at home, recovering from a bilateral mastectomy and a tram flap reconstruction as a result of her breast cancer recurrence in December 1997, like the rest of New Zealand watched on in awe at the footage of the crazy Canadian women.

'I was sitting watching the TV, and it was on The Holmes Show; these wonderful women capsizing. The host was talking about the strength of mind and what have you. It just looked like fun. And I said to my husband and son as we were watching this, I'm going to do that when I'm better.'

Some months later, Trici approached the Cancer Society. 'They didn't know anything about it, and they weren't particularly interested.' Not to be deterred, Trici thought to herself, 'they are in Canada, so it's got to be here.' I was quite determined that it had to be here. I went to them again.

They put me in touch with breast cancer support services, which is part of the Cancer Society. Nita Falcon was an out-there, gorgeous, vivacious woman who did a lot of TV ads, was in theatre groups, and was involved with the breast cancer group. She said, 'Trici, let's do it. We're going to do this.' And that was where it started. Once the Cancer Society saw what was happening, they were right behind us '

At the first meeting to form a team, one of the women volunteered her son as a fitness trainer. So Trici volunteered Graeme, her 25-year-old son, as the coach. He had paddled once before as part of a corporate team. 'I went home and said to him, 'Well, we've got a team, got it all sorted and Graeme, you're the coach'. I can't repeat what his words were. They weren't polite, but I thought, too late, it's already been decided.'

25-year-old Graeme Rountree became the coach of *Busting with Life,* the first breast cancer survivor team outside of North America.

'We were always *first in our lane* for the first couple of seasons. Streets behind everybody else because, at that point, it wasn't competitive. We were out there showing what we could be, and we could paddle after breast cancer,' recalls Trici.

'But then, at the end of our very first season *Abreast In A Boat* was so thrilled that there was a team in New Zealand that they invited us to be their guest in Vancouver.

At the end of our second season, over the winter, we raised $100,000. We went to Vancouver for the International Alcan Dragon Boat Festival in 2000.'

Trici Nelson, through the formation of *Busting with Life*, brought breast cancer out of the closet and into the spotlight in New Zealand. Olympic champion Paul McDonald, Coordinator of the National Dragon Boat Association, became their advisor.

The team in Christchurch was set up in 1999 when Aucklanders Paul McDonald and Ian Ferguson, who had swept for *Abreast In A Boat* during their 1998 visit, issued a challenge to the South Island to set up a team. Dave Sloss, Manager of the Linwood Rugby Club, took up the challenge and contacted the Cancer Society. September 1999 saw *Abreast of Life*, Christchurch officially launched.

When asked if there was a standout moment, Trici Nelson, Founder of the movement in the land of the long white cloud, said, 'There are so many. But the most powerful was participating in my first Flower Ceremony in Vancouver. We hadn't had a Flower Ceremony till we went to Canada. It blew us away. I just thought, how special was that?'

The breast cancer paddler movement continues to grow, and at the time of writing, there are six breast cancer teams in New Zealand.

Leaving New Zealand to fly back to Vancouver, the ticket agent looked at our passports asking, 'are you those crazy Canadian women who paddled in those boats?'

His mother had breast cancer and had not left her house since the day she finished treatment. When he heard about us, he put her in a wheelchair, wheeled her down to the harbour, where they watched every one of our races together.

Our big splash in Windy Wellington Harbour was well worth it.

- Jane Frost, *Abreast In A Boat*

AUSTRALIA

Australia, the vast ancient continent at the opposite end of the world from Canada and just across the 'ditch' from New Zealand, is unique and vastly different from the rest of the world. So not surprisingly, the start of the breast cancer survivor dragon boat movement on this continent was unlike any other breast cancer teams foundation. It began as a national collective rather than as an individual team.

Thanks to a chance meeting with Susan Tulley at a support group meeting run by the Cancer Council, Michelle Hanton was introduced to Australia's emerging breast cancer advocacy movement.

At that meeting, Susan revealed that the First National Breast Cancer Conference for women was being held in Canberra in October 1998. Penny LaSette and Susan were amongst the first consumer representatives trained in Australia by the National Health and Medical Research Council. Penny, Susan, and Michelle collectively felt that as many women from the Northern Territory as possible should attend the Conference.

'As a founding member of NT Breast Cancer Voice', remembers Michelle, 'I got involved with fundraising for the trip. Our relationship with Paspaley Pearls began when they generously donated a pearl pendant for our raffle. Sufficient funds were raised for nine women from the Territory to attend the Conference. There were 300 women from across the country.

Sharon Batt, a Canadian journalist, spoke about the advocacy movement in Canada. She mentioned, 'We even have our own dragon boat teams of survivors,' and flashed up a slide. To this day, I remember the name of that team *Chemo Savvy*. A buzz went around the room. For me, it was a light bulb moment. The concept of a dragon boat appealed immediately.

I knew dragon boat racing existed in the NT because my business had just completed the uniforms for the NT delegation heading to the dragon boat races in Sabah. Dragon boat seemed like something positive, and I needed POSITIVE! At the Conference, the group of women from Darwin all agreed that it sounded like an excellent idea to get a dragon boat up.

Returning home, I diligently researched, determined to form a local team. I learned that a dragon boat required 20 paddlers, so it took a bit to gather a team to participate in a Fun Day held at Lake Alexander in December 1998. Many of the survivors were sceptical and worried about lymphedema. Determined to go ahead, we decided to take on a few supporters. Finally, we got our 20 paddlers, and we were off!

Getting everyone to come to a training session proved to be another obstacle. Paddling out into the middle of Cullen Bay, we wondered how we were going to get back to shore. We were exhausted with the effort of just getting out there – it was all of about 250 metres!'

Race day arrived, and a motley crew, dressed in NT Breast Cancer Voice T-shirts of dubious sizing, turned up at Lake Alexander. SBS Television recording for the program, *Tutti,* captured the team giggling and laughing as they paddled down the racecourse.

Michelle shares, '*Tutti* was my first foray into television interviews. The one regret I have about that day is that no one took any decent photos. We did not realise it would become a moment in history; the start of a national organisation with members in every State and Territory of Australia.'

Michelle thoroughly enjoyed herself and wanted to continue, despite the strenuous exercise, the total lack of coordination, and stamina. The others were unsure of the wisdom of racing in a dragon boat. Undeterred and inspired by her internet findings of *Abreast In A Boat* and *Pink Phoenix,* her only option was to join the local sports dragon boat team.

'It was the only dragon boat group in the NT. I was not very fit. Crawling out of the boat, out of breath, and all red in the face was the norm for me. I regularly sat in the car park for 10 minutes until I'd recovered enough to drive myself home,' are Michelle's vivid memories of her early days of paddling.

'Despite all the aching muscles, lack of breath and exhaustion from the training, I loved the sport. I also realised that dragon boat was a wonderful sport because you could come into it at pretty well any fitness level and build up. It was also unlike other sports, where if you felt tired, you were left behind. Because we were all in the one boat, it was possible to have a little rest and then get back into the paddling—there was no fear of being left behind and having to hurry to catch up with the team.'

Hearing the 2000 World Dragon Boat Titles were being held in Australia and that the Canadians and New Zealanders were sending breast cancer survivor teams, Michelle decided Australia needed a team. After all, it was a matter of national pride; how could Australia, the host nation, not have a team of breast cancer survivors?

Trevor Huggard, President of AusDBF, and Jon Taylor, the then Administrator Director, generously lent support offering information and advice about the sport.

'Sandy Smith, the global liaison for *Abreast In A Boat*, and I exchanged many, many emails,' Michelle fondly shares. 'I was overwhelmed by the supportive attitude and willingness to share information. A package arrived from Canada with copies of the article in the Canadian Medical Journal on the *Abreast In A Boat* study conducted by Dr Don McKenzie. Armed with my information, I talked to anyone and everyone who would listen!'

Anna Wellings Booth from Canberra, Jan Dowd from the Blue Mountains, and Janelle Gamble from Brisbane met with Michelle at the Cancer; We Care Conference 1999 held in Sydney. Breast cancer dragon boating sounded like a marvellous idea! If one area could not get 20 women, they would gather them from around the country; surely they could find 20 survivors to take up the challenge?

April 2000, came around and the Australian National Titles (the World Championships were cancelled). A crew who had never paddled as a team before (actually, they had very little paddling experience at all!) came together at the Sydney International Rowing Centre, Penrith. The debut public appearance of *Dragons Abreast Australia*. The women in this crew came from the Australian Capital Territory, Northern Territory, New South Wales and Queensland.

Janelle Gamble, the only Queenslander in that inaugural *Dragons Abreast* crew back in 2000 (today a seasoned top-level dragon boater with 12 international campaigns as a member of Australia's elite *Auroras*) recalls, 'We were so naive we did not realise we needed to provide our own paddles. Thankfully, Rob Turnbull from *Sydney Dragon Blades* took us under his wing and organised loan paddles from their club.'

Bringing up the rear of each race they entered, the hot pink lycra tops stood out on the water. The big, bold pink statement confirmed that there was indeed life after a diagnosis of breast cancer. The crowds roared as the team paddled their hearts out. The message of living life to the full despite breast cancer, and that early detection was the best protection was well and truly heard thanks to the enormous amount of media coverage generated.

It became evident that composite teams were the only way to be present at significant regattas for quite some time. In 2001 the Chinese New Year Regatta on Darling Harbour saw its first *Dragons Abreast* team. The camaraderie and esprit de corps of these composite teams were incredible. Firm friendships forged, leading to those women becoming the founders of what were to become fully-fledged *Dragons Abreast* teams within their local communities.

It was a slow growth in the early days. You could say it was like pulling teeth to recruit as post breast surgery people continued to be frightened to take up the active sport of dragon boat racing. The medical professionals were still reluctant to recommend dragon boating to their patients despite the research of Dr Don McKenzie with *Abreast In A Boat* in Vancouver, Canada.

By October 2003, with the official launch of *Dragons Abreast Tasmania* in Hobart captured by both ABC and Southern Cross Television, *Dragons Abreast Australia* was completed as a national circle

'It was never a deliberate intention to have teams across Australia.' shares Michelle. 'It was the high levels of media coverage that captured the attention of breast cancer survivors across the country. That coverage was significant because it focused on the possibilities of a fun-filled, active life post-treatment.

Women who felt they needed to go home and wrap themselves in cotton wool could see something positive. We were giving a face to the breast cancer statistics and demonstrating there was plenty of good living to do. Cancer was not necessarily a death sentence.'

Growth of *Dragons Abreast Australia* continued to be a slow and steady build from those early days in 1998 right through to 2004. The catalyst for the enormous growth spurt was the ABC Television, Australian Story episode *In the Pink* airing in June 2004. It catapulted paddling for breast cancer survivors right into the lounge rooms of millions of Australians. With her ready and infectious smile that was ever-present despite the challenges she faced, Jenny Petterson became a beacon of light and hope for those with metastatic breast cancer.

The program followed *Dragons Abreast* members paddling the 55km Ord River Marathon through the magnificent outback setting of the Kimberley, Western Australia. Since the program aired, the paddle has become an iconic event, firmly in the spotlight and on the bucket list for dragon boaters around the globe.

Overnight the interest and demand for breast cancer dragon boating in local communities across the country became overwhelming.

In 2005, *Dragons Abreast Australia* paddled further into maritime history with their inclusion in the display on dragon boat history in Australia at The National Maritime Museum located in Sydney. The Museum singled out *Dragons Abreast Australia* in the dragon boat display alongside Team Australia, representing the Australian Dragon Boat Federation. The showcase remained in place until 2016, when the entire exhibition hall was remodelled.

A National Community Liaison role was created to cope with increasing demand to learn more about breast cancer paddling, the need for funding, and support for fledging groups. Cynthia Kuiper of *Dragons Abreast Sydney* stepped into the position with Lexie Warren of *Dragons Abreast Brisbane,* working alongside her to focus on service clubs including Rotary, Lions, and Zonta.

A frequent outcome of speaking engagements was funding for a local *Dragons Abreast* group within a specific region. Donations generally took the form of cash towards the purchase of equipment, including dragon boats.

Service clubs also provided invaluable support to run events. The most outstanding effort was the combination of Rotary Clubs offering essential volunteers for Abreast In Australia 2007, held in Caloundra, Queensland. The event was, at that time, the world's largest breast cancer survivor regatta.

Dragons Abreast Australia, at its peak, consisted of 45 member groups under the national umbrella. Over the last 23 years, some have merged into sports clubs, some folded, and others have become independent catering for all cancers and competition.

'At the Sarasota IBCPC Regatta, a young woman from the USA diagnosed with terminal Stage 4 breast cancer joined us in the Internationally Abreast boat Inspiration. She could barely paddle but gained so much joy from just being in the boat–carried along with our exhilaration of being out on the water.

We embraced her in some of her darkest moments. She and her husband were literally speechless at the selfless generosity and care wrapped around her. Many tears of sadness and joy were shared that day. This is and should be the epitome of what the movement means and represents.

Welcoming newbies into the fold, focusing on the camaraderie, fun and wellness aspects can only be beneficial all around!'

Judy Smith, *Dragons Abreast NT, Darwin*, Australia

VANGUARD OF THE BREAST CANCER PADDLING MOVEMENT IN AUSTRALIA

State & Territory Founding Coordinators

1998 Northern Territory – Michelle Hanton

1999 Australian Capital Territory – Anna Wellings Booth

2000 Queensland – Janelle Gamble

2001 South Australia – Carlene Butavicius

2001 New South Wales - Martine Boughton

2001 Western Australia – Yvette Libregts

2001 Victoria – Pamela Williams

2003 Tasmania – Louise Woodruff

Founding Board Members

Janelle Gamble (QLD), Michelle Hanton (NT),

Yvonne Dolman (QLD)

Founding Webmaster

Jan Skorich (ACT)

AUSTRALIA

' *Dragons Abreast was one of the positives of breast cancer, and quite honestly, I don't know how things would have gone without you all.* '

Jan Miegel, *Dragons Abreast Port Lincoln*

INTERNATIONALLY ABREAST

This concept for *Internationally Abreast* grew quite by accident. It started when Michelle Hanton, taking the first family holiday since completing her treatment 3 years prior, decided to visit Vancouver. 'I'd had so much support from Sandy Smith of *Abreast In A Boat* in setting up *Dragons Abreast Australia* I wanted to meet her.'

As a business trip to Portland, Oregon was also on Michelle's itinerary, contact was made with *Pink Phoenix* who warmly welcomed her to join their team as a guest paddler.

'My experience paddling as part of *Pink Phoenix* at The Rose Festival in Oregon and a week later at Alcan in Vancouver, made me realise how wonderful it was to have the opportunity to paddle with other teams. It was unimportant that our paddling styles were different, we could all get by. The most important aspect was the camaraderie.

It was a realisation that because of our breast cancer we had joined this wonderful 'club' – the sisterhood of breast cancer dragon boat teams. Wonderful women, all over the globe, ready to offer a warm welcome.

Each of us had looked death in the face. At that moment, we understood what was important. To live life in the moment! We were accepted for who we were – bosom buddies!'

Founding members of *Dragons Abreast Australia*, Penny LaSette and Judy Smith from Darwin were also in Vancouver for the Festival. On the trio's return to Australia with the word of the Conference and dragon boat race to be held in Toronto the following year, the seed was planted for more Australians to travel to races.

What the Aussies did not realise is that most Canadian teams had just enough for their teams and no spare seats. However, *Dragons Abreast Toronto* agreed it was a fine idea to have the Aussies come to Toronto and felt that a team could be modelled on the composite structure that operated within Australia.

In conjunction, with Canadian connections at *Dragons Abreast Toronto*, the very first ever *Internationally Abreast* team debuted in Toronto in 2001. The women that formed the inaugural team came from across Canada and Australia

Akky Mansikka, a founding member of *Dragons Abreast Toronto*, and one of the, at that stage, very few female steers in the dragon boat world, volunteered as the steer.

Such was the excitement that, even though this was the same weekend as their own big race weekend in Vancouver, *Abreast In A Boat*, sent five delegates, Jane Frost, Sandy Smith, Sally Haugen, Sharon Eakins and Lynn Scott as their representatives, to be a part of the first international composite team.

Jacquie Kolber and Eleanor Nielsen from *Dragons Abreast Toronto* worked overtime on promotions, arranging media interviews, including live television crosses and radio interviews. The media zoomed in on this unusual and unique combination of a composite team. A Chinese language newspaper in Canada ran an article on the team; Sandy Smith explained, this was indeed a coup, as breast cancer was not widely talked about in that area of Canadian society.

Team uniforms were sponsored by Regatta Sport, thanks to the wonderful efforts of Jacquie Kolber, *Dragons Abreast Toronto*. Jones New York held a reception for the team; media attention was high. *Internationally Abreast* has gone on to represented breast cancer survivors in Canada, Italy, Germany, Poland, China and in a flotilla down the Thames for Her Majesty Queen Elizabeth II Diamond Jubilee.

'The coach chatted to one or two people, and as he made his way down the boat, I realised he was coming to me. Was I that bad? But it was nothing like that- he smiled and said, 'Well done. I think I can show you something that will make paddling a little easier," – and it did.

Off we paddled again. Afterwards, exhilarated, we made our way to a paddlers' apartment for wine and chips. What an evening – smitten from the start with the sport, by the friendliness of the Breasting the Waves crew, and the positive, thoughtful and kindly encouragement of the coach – key characteristics of a great crew and team which still hold true today. **)**

Jenny Yule, *Abreast In A Boat* 1997- 2017, Vancouver, Canada

THE MAMMOGRAM SONG

Dragon boat songs and chants form a large part of the breast cancer dragon boat tapestry. One that stands out is 'The Mammogram Song' penned by *Chemo Savvy*, Winnipeg, Canada. It stands out because its message is so powerful, and the delivery through song gives pause to listeners, hopefully encouraging many to 'get a mammogram'.

Cathy Prusak, co-author with Peggy Delaney, explains 'It was written for a skit that the team would perform at the Calgary Dragon boat festival in 2000. It was an instant hit, with the women's teams requesting we sing it once we would arrive in marshalling. It was silly and fun but carried a very important message; 'Get a Mammogram!''

The song, performed with Cathy and Peggy as lead singers backed up by team members as the chorus immediately drew media attention. It was upbeat, fun and yet carried a serious message and became a regular feature in news clips that featured *Chemo Savvy*.

'Get a Mammogram!' made its European debut at the 2002 IDBF World Championships in Rome. Sung from the podium at the medal presentations *Internationally Abreast* team members provided the slightly off chorus as Cathy Prusak belted out the words to the delight of the officials that included Australian Ambassador, Murray Cobban, Italian Dragon Boat Federation President, Claudio Schermi plus an array of international journalists and reporters. The team, grinning from ear to ear, and full of life were a clear demonstration that there is a lot of good living to do despite a diagnosis of breast cancer.

Reflecting back, Cathy Prusak shares 'It was always fun to hear other teams singing it, maybe not even knowing its origins. One especially meaningful rendition was sung at the opening of the Abreast In Australia 2007 festival in Caloundra, Australia. This silly song that was part of a skit, was truly embraced by the breast cancer dragon boat world and continues to deliver its poignant message. A message personified, standing in front of you singing - we are still afloat!'

THE MAMMOGRAM SONG
(Sung To The Tune Of Run Around Sue)

Here's the story of a group of gals

Who started out as strangers and developed into pals

A diagnosis of breast cancer was told to everyone

We're together on this journey, it's not ending 'til we've won...

So Hey, Hey, get a mammogram,

Hey, Hey, get a mammogram,

Hey, Hey, get a mammogram,

Hey, aaaahhhhhhh

Went to the doctor just the other day,

he said 'I've found a lump, I'm afraid to say'

'It's in the breast and we've got to see'

'So come back Friday at a quarter to three'

So Hey, Hey, get a mammogram,

Hey, Hey, get a mammogram,

Hey, Hey, get a mammogram,

Hey—aaaahhhhhhh

Once a month here is the plan, yeah

You do a breast self exam

Check every month at the same time

'cause the worst lump's, the one you don't find

Here's the moral of the story from our dragon boat

We found a lump and we're still afloat

So listen people what we're telling you

Check your breasts it's the smart thing to do

So Hey, Hey, get a mammogram,

Hey, Hey, get a mammogram,

Hey, Hey, get a mammogram,

Hey, aaaaaaaahhhhhhh Hey!!!

ENGLAND

The breast cancer paddling movement began in the United Kingdom in 2004 in Liverpool.

Eve Elliott Pearson, with support from the local dragon boat team *Amathus*, founded *Pool of Life*. A successful grant allowed the team to purchase their own boat.

Anne Holt, an original member of *Pool of Life*, 'Not being from a sporting background, breast cancer and *Pool of Life* opened the door for me into a new world of support, friendship, camaraderie and dragon boat racing. Despite having had breast cancer, I feel lucky and thankful to be part of *Pool of Life*. It's changed my life for the better.'

In October 2004, Eve Elliott Pearson, via the Fire Service physiotherapist, asked for anyone living with a breast cancer diagnosis to join a dragon boat team for survivors in Liverpool. Sue Cogley, diagnosed four years earlier, was immediately intrigued when she received the message at work.

Peter Cogley takes up the tale, 'Sue answered the call and discovered this would be the first breast cancer dragon boat team in the UK. *Pool of Life* met at the Queens Dock Liverpool on Halloween 2004. Twenty women from different walks of life but with one thing in common, each had survived breast cancer.

The first paddle was a very nervous affair, to begin with, but as the novice crew approached the jetty after paddling around the dock, I could see the widest smiles from stem to stern. Sue was hooked, therefore the Cogley family was committed to this new venture for good. It helped that it wasn't just Sue who loved paddling. My daughter Jane, who was 13 years old at the time, and I loved it too.

The group was diverse, some partaking as individuals or with existing buddies who had been supporting each other in other cancer support groups. There were also several partners, families and friends. Everyone was eager to get involved with a new adventure.

Weekly training and racing at venues across the UK, in the National League, followed with the encouragement and guidance of the Great Britain National Coaches from the *Amathus* racing team, who also happened to be the national champions and based in Liverpool.

Sue was a driving force in the team and along with several others was very keen to spread the word about breast cancer paddling across the UK. Even though the racing was exciting, it could engender competition within the team and result in some exclusivity. This was not what Sue wanted as she was determined that participation for all and recreation, support and inclusivity should be the priorities of any future team.'

Paddlers for Life was born in 2007 in the English Lake District on Windermere, England's largest lake.

Louisa Balderson explains 'In 2007 Sue Cogley, Christine Robinson, (both sadly passed now) and I, rehearsed our vision, for the umpteenth time. All that practising, and I mean, not just the survivor paddling, but acknowledging the essential role of our supporters. Understanding the range of feelings people experience and embracing the familiar uncertainty that a diagnosis of breast cancer brings.'

Using the lessons learned and experience gained, the three founders, in Louisa's words, 'were passionate participants in the act, breathing the fire of the dragon's spirit: an offering of adventure to others, during their moment of need.'

That same effort is visible now. That same ache of success is felt right now, too, as *Paddlers for Life* welcomes new paddlers to sit abreast in our dragon boat beauties— always *first in our lane* on Lake Windermere.'

Peter Cogley acknowledges that the sponsorship of the English Lakes Hotel Group and a charity called Building On Overlooked Sporting Talent (BOOST) and others ensured the team got off the ground.

'Although Sue had several episodes of recurrence, she never lost her passion and her ambition to spread the word continued. Sue was instrumental in raising the profile of breast cancer paddling in the UK. We took the roadshow far and wide, helping to establish several new teams from Scotland to the south coast of England and even beyond the UK in Dublin. I was happy to ride on her coattails and was so proud of her endless energy and enthusiasm,' remembers Peter.

Sadly, Sue lost her long battle with breast cancer in February 2018, but her legacy lives on. Peter Cogley continues to support and help the team, often taking the helm and encouraging new paddlers. Their daughter Jane has been made a *Paddlers for Life* UK patron and keeps her mother's passion and vision alive.

POOL OF LIFE

A poem by Caroline McTomney, *Pool of Life* '

Pool of Life is a dragon boat team

for men and women who love to dream.

We've all been touched by breast cancer, in one way or another.

Maybe it was you or your sister or your brother.

Being diagnosed with cancer can be so hard, it's true.

But there are so many positive groups and experiences that are new.

If you only open your eyes, you'll see what's out there for you.

Finding your place upon the water, with people you never knew.

I love sitting in the boat, in my kit that's mostly pink.

Looking around at all of you, it surely makes me think.

Feeling all kinds of weather on my face, it makes me feel alive.

It's so much fun and it's exercise too, it can only help you thrive.

On the first Sunday of the month, we take part in the Pink Paddle, where we visit the Albert Dock.

We all have a coffee and a chat, before you know it, it's time to go as you look up at the clock!

We're soon all clambering back, to sit inside the boat.

Our wonderful pink army, all ready to take float.

I've abseiled to raise money, as a trip to Florence was planned.

Racing with women from around the world, the feeling was so grand.

It's something I will never forget, precious memories I'll always treasure.

I'm so proud to be part of *Pool of Life*, it brings me so much pleasure.

Don't get me wrong, sad things happen too, losing people along the way.

But cancer can also bring us closer together, helping to brighten up our day.

So if you see me on the docks, I'll have a smile upon my face,

Because if I'm paddling with all of you, I'll be in my happy place.

SCOTLAND

Andrina Gordon, of Edinburg, Scotland, was recommended to exercise to reduce her lymphoedema in one arm. Wearing a compression sleeve was her only option apart from the gym, which Andrina hated. Her physiotherapist then suggested dragon boating.

Unfortunately, the nearest team was *Paddlers for Life* at Lake Windermere. Determined to give dragon boating a try, Andrina drove to Windermere in 2009 and became hooked.

In March 2010, three breast cancer survivors (whose names we have been unable to ascertain) formed *Dragons Boats on Loch Ken* to raise funds and set up the first-ever permanent dragon boat team in Scotland.

The *Port Edgar Dragons*, started by Andrina Gordon, was launched in 2011. A small, hardcore group of paddlers taking to the water on a near-weekly basis (weather and tides permitting – it is Scotland after all!) with many more who support the team in the background.

As their website says, 'We are an exercise group, we are a social gathering, we are laugh generating, two hours of water-based hilarity, a network of people who share a common cause; a cause which we embrace but does not define us.'

The *Port Edgar Dragons* and *Dragon Boats on Loch Ken* are community teams, not exclusively for breast cancer paddlers.

DRAWN TO THE BAY

Deborah Bonner, Founder, *Donegal Dragons*

My Dream was to sing in a band and become a Dancer
But at 40 I was told, "you've got Breast Cancer. "
So feeling robbed of security, I was drawn to the bay
Feeling loss and anxiety, I'd hoped I'd be ok

While on the rolling waves, sometimes dripping with tears
I was determined to Dig Deep and overcome my fears
With God on my side, it was time to take a stand
With a fight for life and a paddle in hand.

Awakening my Life Forces as I get in the Boat
Liberated and laughter would keep me Afloat
Paddling in sync while energising the seeds
In my happy place, I fulfil my needs.

I'll Dig Deep every stroke on our Beautiful Bay
While the scars are forgotten on that paddling day
So fuelled for health but with loss of hair
I'm out on the water, and I just don't care.

I'll push myself to the limit
Ready Attention Go
Eyes In your own Boat
And it's away with the Flo
Pull harder. Reach Further. I will go all out
I won't let my team down; the helm lets out a shout!

My arms, legs and body will all start to scream
But the water supports me to win back my Dream.
We approach midway we are neck in neck
My surgery side stinging, but what the heck.

We must keep paddling as the crowd watches the race
Defeating dark shadows, we pick up the pace
No time for faffing as we see the finish line
Bury that blade, and all will be fine.

The horn blows.
We've got this
We've won
It was tight
I knew that my paddle buddies would help with the fight.

With happy hearts and a HipHip Hooray
We are all in the same Boat on any given day
So hold your heads up and stick out your chests
Donegal Dragons are the Best

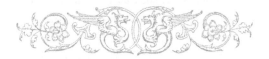

IRELAND

Dublin, the Irish capital city, sitting at the mouth of the River Liffey, is home to the first breast cancer dragon boat team in Ireland.

When Fiona Tiernan's breast cancer recurred in 2009, she decided to create a dragon boat racing team for women recovering from breast cancer. Fiona didn't have a paddle, a crew, a boat or any money. But she had vision, courage, tenacity and incredible powers of persuasion.

Fiona persuaded her friend, Marian O'Dea, and an experienced dragon boat coach, Julie Doyle, to form Ireland's first dragon boat club.

Within six months, Fiona secured family and friends' support plus funding from HSE and Breast Cancer Ireland for two dragon boats.

Plurabelle Paddlers officially launched in 2010. The dragon boats, *Anna* and *Livia*, and team name are inspired by the fictional character created by legendary Irish novelist James Joyce. In the 1939 novel Finnegans Wake, Anna Livia Plurabelle symbolises the eternal and universal female.

Under Fiona's initial leadership and latterly under the leadership of Marian O'Dea, Margaret Mulcahy, and Susan Rowe, the *Plurabelle Paddlers* have thrived. Today, they are a vibrant and welcoming club. It was no surprise to those who know the *Plurabelle Paddlers* that the club reached the final five in the Irish Times Best Sports Club in Ireland competition.

As Ireland's first dragon boat club, *Plurabelle Paddlers* has consistently sought to offer support and encouragement to the growing dragon boat family in Ireland. This includes practical help, including donating *Anna* (their old boat) to a newly formed club in need of a boat. Some years later, *Anna* was gifted from that club to yet another freshly formed dragon boat club.

Based on Dublin's Grand Canal Dock, *Plurabelle Paddlers*, Ireland's first breast cancer club, was the first dragon boat club to register with the Irish Dragon Boat Association (IDBA).

By 2012 a temporary clubhouse at the end of Hanover Quay was secured. With a lot of work and generous donations, it became the base for the team off-the-water training. Their Winter Fitness Training Programme was selected as one of the winners of the 2013 Arthur Guinness Projects.

In 2019 a brand-new purpose-built clubhouse just across the dock on Charlotte's Quay became the new home for the *Plurabelle Paddlers*, providing a space for meetings, a cup of tea and a catch-up venue for those members unable to paddle to keep in touch.

The *Plurabelle Paddlers* have been instrumental in the sport's growth for breast cancer survivors in Ireland. Teams in Donegal and Belfast established as a direct result of the formation of *Team Ireland* for the 2014 IBCPC Participatory Dragon Boat Festival in Sarasota, Florida, USA.

Anna Connolly sums it up 'It's not for us the 'poor me' mentality. We are determined not to let cancer win - life wins every time. We tick every box: outdoor fun, get fit, make friends, inclusive, affordable, supportive, and community-based. All shapes and sizes, Northside, Southside, professional, unemployed, race, nationality, bald, hairy, bald again!! We are winners every day.'

GOING FOR HOME

Rivers of tears have overflowed our Dock today

Fallen friends had joy and laughter on these precious still waters

Digging deep /now flying high

Heaven sent but earthly missed

An Angel boat of womanly beings.

But not for us the victim's dark lament

Soaring from the depths – a Dragons Head appears

Helping hands that push and steer – Go for Home! Go for Home!

Branded by this hand of fate that all of us have come to hate

Tears come and silence fall on the vacant rows ....

Season through season …in sickness and in health they came

Echoing cheers from under the bridge through driving rain and clear sunshine

Then steamy coffee in a rundown shed and a pillow of kinship for under your head

Your presence was dear to us, near to us but taken from us

Hold the boat and lower your head …a sleeping Dragon is never dead

Slumbering silently - while onward our journey goes

In hope as much as in fear that fate will not come calling for us

Vacant rows are more and more, but newbies come where they once were

To fill great shoes with wide-eyed eagerness.

Cancer calls and cancer takes but never will remove you from my mind

Our time is now as we raise that boat -all forty-four hands to get her afloat

Dream on our loves – dream big, dream small

Anna and *Livia* hear your call.

Anna Connolly, *Plurabelle Paddlers*, Dublin, Ireland

NORTHERN IRELAND

Joanne Rock, from Belfast, experienced first-hand the power and benefits of being part of a dragon boat team when she participated at the 2014 IBCPC Participatory Dragon Boat Festival in Sarasota, Florida, USA.

On her return from Sarasota, Joanna set about forming a team. The first breast cancer paddling team in Northern Ireland launched in March 2015.

Lagan Dragons, named after the river on which they paddle, is based in Belfast. The club has grown from small beginnings in 2015 to owning three of its own dragon boats and having over fifty members.

EUROPE

The seed for the breast cancer survivors dragon boat movement in Europe was planted when *Internationally Abreast* attended the World Club Crew Championships in Rome, Italy, in September 2002.

The crew, who had never paddled together before, had a common goal – to live life to the fullest and encourage the search for a cure whilst promoting the fact that women can still lead full and active lives despite a diagnosis of breast cancer.

Australian paddlers from *Dragons Abreast Brisbane* and Gold Coast, ACT, Victoria, NT and NSW, Canadians from *Abreast In A Boat, Chemo Savvy, Waves of Hope,* and *Dragons Abreast Toronto* made up *Internationally Abreast* 2002. This momentous visit was newsworthy, enabling extensive media coverage in each of the home bases of the paddlers as well as on the ground in Italy.

Determined to maximise the breast cancer message, Michelle Hanton, wrote to notify the Australian Ambassador to Rome, HE Murray Cobban, of the teams' participation. Operating under the premise, the worst thing that could happen would be no response; Michelle cheekily asked if the Ambassador would hold a function for the team at the Embassy.

A reply came back from the Australian Embassy in Rome that Mrs Cobban was undergoing chemotherapy treatment for breast cancer. They would be delighted to welcome us to Rome, helping us promote our message any way they could.

His Excellency Mr Murray Cobban and Mrs Maureen Cobban hosted a reception for *Internationally Abreast* at the official residence, complete with gilt-edged formal invitations bearing the Australian coat of arms. Senior dragon boat representatives, including the President of the Italian Dragon Boat Federation, Mr Claudio Schermi, Mr. Zhang Faqiang, President of the International Dragon Boat Federation, and Italian television and documentary crews, were guests.

Michelle Hanton recalls 'It was so exciting to have the opportunity to address this distinguished group of guests. When I told Paspaley Pearls, a sponsor of *Dragons Abreast* where I was going, they insisted on lending me a string of pearls to wear for the occasion. I flew to Rome with a $10,000 necklace that I was terrified of losing!'

So impressed were the Chinese contingent that at the IDBF meeting the next day, President of the Chinese Dragon Boat Federation, Mr Zhang, announced that China would invite breast cancer teams to the 5th World Championships in 2003 in Shanghai.

A Canadian documentary crew followed the team for the three days of racing. This was thanks to *Abreast In A Boat* advising the producer, Donna Leon, of the Rome event. The documentary wanted to focus on a team just starting up. *Internationally Abreast* was definitely a novelty as team members had never paddled together previously.

Donna had identified *Cape Breastoner,* from Cape Breton in Nova Scotia, as the start up team and wanted to contrast this with a team that was established. As *Internationally Abreast* was something different, the adventure to Rome fitted the bill perfectly!

The film crew, consisting of two remarkable women, seemed to film non-stop. Team members became somewhat paranoid about looking around to see if the sound was 'on' before launching into any conversation as 'muffy', the sound recorder, had a habit of appearing out of nowhere! The documentary, T*hey've Got Game; Water Works,* was aired on the North American networks that winter.

A history-making moment in Rome was the 2000 metre race. Although there were other breast cancer survivor teams present, only *Internationally Abreast* entered the 2000 metre race. The other breast cancer teams could not understand the logic of going in a race where you were bound to come last. But for *Internationally Abreast,* this presented another not-to-be-missed opportunity to fly the breast cancer flag. The team was there to spread awareness of this insidious disease, not to win races.

'The race course was two 500 meter lanes with a narrow turn in the middle and we had to paddle the course twice for 2000 metres.' shares Elspeth Humphries, who swept this history-making crew. 'I was really nervous about hitting another boat at the turn, but then I realised they would all be ahead of us by then! We paddled with style and strength. The world-class sports teams cheered us with great gusto!'

Predictably the team came last, even though they had been amongst the first to set off. Still, the love, support, and cheering received from the shoreline put them in first place in the hearts of everyone present.

After one of the first races, a short, vibrant, highly excited Italian woman charged up to the group. She introduced herself as Orlanda Capelli in very excited Italian, a breast cancer survivor drumming for the Italian team. Linda Acosta from *Abreast In A Boat,* who spoke Spanish—close enough to understand translated that Orlanda wanted to join us. The fact she had no race pass as *Internationally Abreast* was of little consequence: she was a local, spoke the language, soon had the officials all sorted out, and the race pass clutched proudly in her hand.

Orlanda became the drummer for *Internationally Abreast* and remained so for the next few races. The dragon fire burnt strongly, fuelling Orlanda to establish the first breast cancer survivor team in Italy—*Pink Butterfly.*

FLYING HIGH

Flying high, no longer alone,
in the company of great heroes,
great warriors.
Women strong and free,
touching the sky.
The fierce dragon who reared its head
from the dungeon of death
to destroy and devour me,
guarding its great secrets,
is now taking me places I never dreamed of
The messenger of death, destruction and loss,
transformed to gentle vapor,
clouds in the sky
Now helping me fly high
Friends, family, children
nurturing, energising, transforming,
opening doors
to places I never dreamed of,
removing unseen barriers

Barriers, walls of fear and ignorance,
unseeing eyes, distrust,
all dissolving in the mist.
A phoenix risen from the ashes of death.
The dragon is tamed, transformed,
like the butterfly out of its cocoon
Our ally, our friend, and so it transforms us,
It is us, we are the dragon.
A dragon that has control, direction,
and purpose,
Light, hope, choices, power, strength
Fire
Water
Sky
Earth
Life
Energy

Akky Mansikka, *Dragons Abreast Toronto*, Steer *Internationally
Abreast*, Toronto & Rome

ITALY

The work of Dr Don McKenzie was crucial to Orlanda being able to recruit Italian women since the advice of the day was not to strain the affected arm to avoid the risk of lymphoedema. It was also taboo to talk about cancer, let alone talk about sport for breast cancer survivors.

Orlanda tried to contact breast cancer associations and oncologists with little success, but that changed when she met the ANDOS Association in Rome. A group of members were willing to try dragon boating under the supervision of the ANDOS doctors.

There were not enough women to create a team, so Orlanda searched for other women to join.

One of these was Ivana Policiti. 'I met Orlanda at the Komen Race in May 2003. She was there with her brochures explaining her idea for the birth of the new team in anticipation of the championships in China.

I was stunned! I had undergone the removal of many lymph nodes and was forbidden to do anything strenuous.'

Orlanda was persistent in persuading Ivana to share her contact details. Ivana, who had always been a sportswoman —tennis, swimming, running—went home feeling depressed. At 42 years old, all opportunities for a physically active life were closed to her because of breast cancer, at least that was what she thought.

'When I got home, I talked to my husband and children, who pushed me to try dragon boating but also suggested I talk to my oncologist. My oncologist shut down the discussion by saying that if lymphedema developed, I would have it for life. He refused to discuss it further.'

By early October 2003, Orlanda had gathered a team, including Ivana, varying in age from 30 to over 60. The first meeting was held at the EUR Lake, facilitated by Claudio Schermi, President of the Italian Dragon Boat Federation. Terrified of falling into the water Ivana cautiously stretched her paddle forward from the pool's edge during the practice. 'The late Andrea Apolloni assisted Orlanda as the team climbed into the dragon boat for the first time. I remember it as a somewhat comic moment,' smiled Ivana with fond recollection. 'Paddles held the wrong way. Not stretching and being hit by the paddle of the person behind you. Some did not want to get wet, but slowly we moved the boat and started to feel more secure. '

The official debut of *Pink Butterfly* took place at the Christmas Cup held in December 2003 at EUR Lake. 'Our paddling was out of time, but we managed to complete the 200 metres to the applause of the public,' is Ivana's recollection.

Suspicion greeted team members as they became spokeswomen attempting to create contacts with oncologists, physiotherapists, and fellow breast cancer survivors. At a conference of sports medicine physicians both in Rome and in Jesolo, Venice, where Orlanda spoke, her words fell on deaf ears.

Fortunately, many athletes believed in the team and were willing to help spread the word. 'We started touring Italy to share our mission,' shared Ivana. Through their club connections, athletes organised meetings allowing us to talk to both doctors and other women. Slowly the message spread, and those who saw us realised that there was a psychological side to the sport. We were more active, confident and certainly more cheerful.

Amongst those athletes who believed in us were Olympians Daniele Scarpa & Sandra Truccolo. Four breast cancer paddlers, including myself, were invited to join the dragon boat crew, captained by Daniela Paciotti, taking part in the 2004 *Vogalonga*, a 35 km iconic paddle through the waterways of Venice.'

Sandra Truccolo and Daniele Scarpa have consistently lent their voices to promote the breast cancer cause, encouraging survivors to participate in many sporting adventures involving paddle crafts that demonstrate there is definitely a full and active life to be led despite a diagnosis of breast cancer.

The medical circles, especially sports medicine, began to look at the activities of Orlanda and *Pink Butterfly* with more positivity. 'I remember one of the doctors who challenged us in Jesolo, Venice in 2009, came up to apologise for the scepticism he'd previously shown. Oncologists now encourage cancer patients or former cancer patients to play sports to help prevent a recurrence,' grinned Ivana as she recalled the early years for this book.

In February 2008, *Pink Butterfly* decided to leave the ANDOS Association in Rome. They will always be grateful for the early support. Still, it was time to create the Pagaie Rosa Dragon Boat Onlus Association focussing on psycho-physical recovery through dragon boat and other paddle sports.

Word of *Pink Butterfly* reached the banks of the Arno, where the Canottieri Comunali Firenze had recently added dragon boating to its activities. The Canottieri team, famous for distinguished athletes on both the national and international competition fields, heard, with scepticism, the echoes of the message of women in pink.

At the turn of the new millennium, the Tuscan health administration began to focus on cancer prevention. Doctors and physiotherapists began taking an interest. The Florentine chapter of the Italian League for the Fight against Cancer (LILT), established in 1927, marked the beginning of the new millennium with an increase in its activities.

Held annually in Florence since 2003, the Corri la Vita, which includes a marathon and walk through the streets of the city centre, carries a public message of prevention and rehabilitation. The event had begun to break the taboos of silence on breast cancer with free mammography screening and speeches from the stage in scenic Piazza Santa Croce.

In 2005, *Pink Butterfly*, led by Orlanda Cappelli, were invited to attend the Corri la Vita on Sunday, 2 October, to provide a dragon boat demonstration. The paddle took place under the Ponte Vecchio, ensuring immense public visibility.

ITALY

Simultaneously, the Oncological Rehabilitation Center (CeRiOn) established new headquarters in Villa le Rose as a centre of excellence. The rehabilitation activities offered ensured breast cancer had a prominent place. Donna Come Prima, the volunteer service within the centre, provided support to women who had undergone breast cancer surgery. It became the nucleus of *Florence Dragon Lady*.

Canottieri Comunali willingly offered technical support to train a newly formed Florence team establishing an agreement with LILT Firenze. On 14 February 2006, Valentine's Day, *Florence Dragon Lady LILT* officially launched

Orlanda Capelli passed away in September 2008. 'Despite the initial bewilderment, we all continued to carry on Orlanda's work,' said Ivana Policiti. 'I became the President, always honoring her teaching, continuing collaborations with the various hospitals in Rome that also carried out medical studies on our activities and recommend our sporting activity to BCS women.'

Cecilia Picchi, instrumental in supporting the establishment of new breast cancer teams in Europe, joined *Florence Dragon Lady LILT* in 2008. 'I heard about the team at Corri la Vita. I'd always loved sports and decided to try dragon boating.' Her professional experience teaching Italian to adults at the European University Institute combined with speaking English, Spanish and French, and her native Italian made Cecilia an ideal candidate for the newly created role of European Representative on the International Breast Cancer Paddlers Commission (IBCPC). She held the position from 2015 to 2020. 'My role offered guidance and support. Helping ensure new team understood and were aligned with *Abreast In A Boat's* original mission and vision—that our race is against breast cancer and not each other.'

The movement started in Italy by Orlanda Capelli after meeting *Internationally Abreast* in 2002 continues to grow throughout Italy. The influence of *Florence Dragon Lady* and *Pink Butterfly* have played a significant role in the spread of breast cancer survivor dragon boating across Europe. There are currently 30 breast cancer teams in Italy.

FRANCE

The dragon spirit began to spread its wings in France after Sylvie Cappellone, a psychologist from Reims, travelled to Florence to learn Italian. She became friends with Luigia Maggiore, a member of the *Florence Dragon Lady LILT* team.

Hearing of the wonderful experience Luigia had paddling in a dragon boat post breast cancer treatment filled Sylvie with enthusiasm to create the same opportunity in Reims. The local cancer association, sparked with dragon fire created by Sylvie, invited *Florence Dragon Lady* to visit Reims.

Formal and informal meetings in December 2008 inspired local breast cancer survivors to form *Ensemble pour Elles*. The team had the goal to attend the Florence Dragon Boat Pink Meeting and paddle the Vogalonga 2009 alongside their newfound Italian sister paddlers.

A French television crew travelled with the French team and experienced adventure on the waterways of Venice when they sank just 4 km from the finish line in rough seas. The documentary 'Nous irons à Venise' retraces the epic adventures of the first French breast cancer paddling team tackling the Vogalonga 2009.

A fictional film, 'Vogue la vie' about a group of women ages 27 to 77—based loosely on the paddlers' experiences was, in 2014, released in French cinemas. The film inspired a wave of interest across the country.

New breast cancer paddling teams started appearing, with their goal being 'to take part in the Vogalonga'. At the time of writing, there are over 50 independent breast cancer survivor teams in France.

GERMANY

Although dragon boating for breast cancer survivors was already well established in Europe, and even though breast cancer survivor teams visited Berlin, Germany as part of the IDBF World Corcoms in 2005, Germany did not join the pink paddler movement until Hannelore Braselmann came along.

Hannelore successfully established *Die Pinkpaddlerinnen* in 20210—paddling against breast cancer—in Wiesbaden, located in central-western Germany in the Frankfurt RhineMain Region.

Hannelore, a volunteer canoe trainer since 1973 and a dragon boat trainer since 1994 at the Wiesbaden-Schierstein water sports club, visited Canada in 2009 to participate in the World Police and Fire Games in Vancouver. She was a trainer for the German police and fire department national team.

Their hosts on Salt Spring Island invited them to a celebration where Hannelore met several Canadian breast cancer survivors talking about the pink paddler movement. Hannelore said, 'As a fellow survivor, I knew what they were talking about; I was very impressed by this idea. On my return to Germany, I campaigned for women affected by breast cancer to have the opportunity to go dragon boating in Germany'.

Peter Deutschmann, Hannelore's husband, a masseur and lymphatic drainage therapist, regularly treated patients with breast cancer. He provided valuable support and tips on what to pay particular attention to when training breast cancer paddlers with bodies compromised by surgery.

Hannelore's initiative spread across the country, and there are currently more than 20 breast cancer paddling teams in Germany.

POLAND

The story of dragon boat for breast cancer survivors in Poland began in a most unlikely manner. As a result of SARS, the World Nations Dragon Boat Championships in 2003 relocated from Shanghai to Poznan.

Abreast In A Boat, planning to spread their outreach to China, had formed *Abreast to Shanghai* on the understanding that there would be several breast cancer teams from Australia and Asia. However, these teams withdrew because the Championships moved to Poznan, Poland.

A quick name change to *Abreast to Poland* saw organisers in Vancouver reaching out to the HPOLITA Kościański Association, whose primary role was providing psycho-physical rehabilitation to breast cancer patients as well as raising awareness. In Poznan, they had a social centre providing counselling and support. Before *Abreast In A Boat* got in touch, the organisation had hardly even heard of dragon boating!

Two Polish breast cancer teams quickly came together under the name *Amazonki*, and a breast cancer division was created.

Jenny Yule, *Abreast In A Boat*, recalls, 'The Amazonki were marvellous—great people, fun and hospitable. We learnt a lot about their post-operative support, and visited their centre which was warm and welcoming. They loved paddling and, in the breast cancer division race, won silver and bronze medals. They decided to come to *10 Years Abreast in Vancouver* two years later.'

Besides paddling together, the team gathered once a month to celebrate birthdays, invite interesting guests, discuss their plans and dreams. They also did gymnastics and music for rehabilitation and relaxation.

Team member, Iwona Borowska living in Kościan, about fifty kilometres from Poznan shared, 'We call ourselves 'Amazons', after the mythology of women without breasts, the queen of whom was Hippolyta, hence the name of our club. These were brave women, like us. They did not surrender, and neither do we.'

Although the Polish dragon boat program for breast cancer survivors faltered after the 10 Year Anniversary of *Abreast In A Boat* that *Amazonki* attended, there is still interest in dragon boat paddling. A group of breast cancer survivors travelled from Poland to attend a conference in Florence organised by *Florence Dragon Lady*, took part in a paddling activity and explained that although there was interest, the costs of getting on the water was too expensive for it to become a regular activity

'I have gained an understanding of the priority in my life; solidarity, friendship, the road from illness to be a dragon lady. This road is not always easy to travel. The team has phases and sometimes stormy phases, but strength and solidarity come first. Through dragon boat, I've had the opportunity to meet women from all over the world. To be welcomed and paddle with many teams, so now I have lots of pink sisters everywhere!'

Milena Vacirca, *Florence Dragon Lady,* Italy

AUSTRIA

Australia and New Zealand play a significant part in how Svenja Franke-Bruhn, founder of the first breast cancer survivor team in Austria, was motivated to start the *Vienna Pink Dragons*.

'I had my diagnosis in NZ in 2011 and finished treatment there before moving to Sydney in July 2012,' shares Svenja. 'Knowing of the team *CanSurvive* in Wellington, I approached *Dragons Abreast Sydney* and started paddling at the end of 2012. That got me hooked! It also helped enormously to keep my lymphoedema under control.'

Cynthia Kuiper of *Dragons Abreast Sydney*, knowing Svenja was moving to Vienna, actively encouraged her to form a team in Vienna. As a founding member of *Dragons Abreast Sydney*, Cynthia shared everything she could think of about getting a breast cancer survivor paddling group up and running in new territory.

Cynthia recalls, 'She was very doubtful it would be doable in Austria. But I assured her she was just the girl to do it, introduced her to Milena Vacirca from *Florence Dragon Lady*, and the rest is history!'

Svenja shares 'Sometimes I wonder why. Why not only breast cancer but also severe lymphoedema? Without it, I would not have been driven to contact the *Vienna Dragons* and start this project with Nina. Maybe I would never have met her—Nina and her husband Felix were both members of the *Vienna Dragons* and the rowing club. I approached them while still living in Sydney. Unlike Germany, the dragon boat sport is not well known in Austria. I knew I needed help with equipment, knowledge etc to start a pink team.'

'Nina holds a very special place in my heart. We shared a special connection, and the age difference did not matter,' remembers Svenja fondly. 'Nina was a fit young woman, pregnant with her first child when told she only had three months to live. A non-smoker, she was diagnosed with lung cancer. Thanks to a mutation, she was able to take a specific first-line medication, by coincidence developed by the company Boehringer Ingelheim for whom she worked as a scientist. She fought for a year before the medication stopped working. Her eyesight had been affected, and she was nearly blind when she participated in our first pink festival in 2017.'

Austria was a country where many doctors and patients were still doubtful of the benefits of exercise. *Vienna Pink Dragons* gained support for a breast cancer category of races to be included at the 2017 Drachenboot Cup held annually in Vienna. The event was intended to provide a platform to showcase a vivid example of the benefits of dragon boating after a breast cancer diagnosis.

The Florence-based IBCPC European representative, Cecilia Picchi, promoted the event as 2017's big international event for European teams. Over 130 BCS Italian paddlers from 11 different teams accepted the invitation, plus a representative from *AmaBele Belles* in South Africa.

Dr Nina Kerrens passed away at age 36 on 20 May 2018. It was the day Svenja paddled the Vogalonga with *Pink Ribbonettes* Bruxelles. 'She left us two gorgeous and uplifting presents to keep going,' smiles Svejna fondly. 'A boat, and most importantly her vibrant, funny, cute daughter, little Lara (now 4 and a half), our little mascot. Lara often accompanies us on the water with her father, Felix, our helm and trainer. We all love standing beside Felix and Lara, and we hope they will remain with us for a long time.'

Commemorating the memory of Dr Nina Kerrens is the gift of a dragon boat from her family to the *Vienna Pink Dragons*, which is aptly named 'Nina.'

There is currently, at the time of writing, only one breast cancer paddling team in Austria.

BELGIUM

The breast cancer paddling movement took root in Belgium when Rosette Van Rossem, President and founding member of the Pink Ribbon Belgium Association, envisioned creating breast cancer survivor dragon boat teams. Her plan began with inviting ten survivors from across Belgium to accompany her on a 5-day trip to Venice, where they had the opportunity to try out dragon boating and meet the Venetian team, *Pink Lioness*.

The women were warmly received in Venice by Lucia Furlan and *Pink Lioness* at their team clubhouse RSC Bucintoro. An exchange of official plaques and other gifts marked the beginning of a close friendship between the women of Belgium and their Venetian hosts.

Smiles and hugs brought down language barriers *'En quelques minutes, nous sommes devenues des sœurs de cœur'* 'in a few minutes we became sisters of the heart' Cécile and Sophie, two members of the group exclaimed.

Monique Quayhaegens from Lier and Carine Van Hoppe from Turnhout, part of the delegation to Venice, returned filled with dragon fire. Having discovered the benefits of paddling a dragon boat, they spent the winter developing a plan to start a team in Belgium.

Pink Lioness Belgique was initially chosen as the name in honour of their *Pink Lioness* sisters in Venice. The women of Venice had opened their hearts, willingly shared knowledge and forged a strong bond of friendship with their Belgian paddling sisters. As teams became established, the official name adopted was *Pink Ribbonnetes*, followed by the name of the city Bruxelles, Lier and Turnhout, where each group was based.

Monique contacted the Royal Canoe Club of Lier and Carine found a home base with the Technico Kajak Club of Turnhout. Both clubs warmly welcomed Monique and Carine. Although there were no dragon boats, they provided the *Pink Ribbonettes* with canoes, helms, necessary equipment and training to get on the water.

On 5 June 2016, eight *Ribbonettes* in Lier and nine in Turnhout officially launched *Pink Ribbonettes* with their maiden voyage in canoes, enthusiastically encouraged by family, club members and sponsors. The same year, Lili De Boeck, thanks to the support of Cercles des Régates Bruxelles Kayak, started the group *Pink Ribbonettes Brussels*.

Paddling in Belgium takes place on the canals. For the most part, the canals are relatively narrow, making manoeuvring a dragon boat for turns a challenge. It is for this reason that most groups, except Brussels, paddle in canoes.

SPAIN

Spain boasts a rich cultural history, vibrant cities, monuments, waterways, and beaches, including dragon boats filled with pink paddlers.

In March 2016, as part of the International Festival of San Pedro del Pinatar organised by the Spanish Association of Dragon Boat, the 1st International Forum on Cancer and Sport took place. Numerous breast cancer paddling teams from England, Italy, France and a Canadian team attended.

Inspired by the visiting breast cancer survivor teams participating at the San Pedro del Pinatar Dragon Boat Festival, Spanish survivors formed *Flamenco Rosa* in April 2016.

Most of the founding members belonged to a group of cancer survivors called Mucho por Vivir (Much Living to do). Seeing other breast cancer teams paddling convinced them they could do this also. The goal was accomplished with support from *Dragon Queens* and the Pinatar Dragon boat teams in San Pedro.

The process of recruiting women at the beginning was challenging. Doctors did not suggest sports activities in Spain as part of the rehabilitation, post breast cancer surgery, much less a sport as new as dragon boat. Fortunately, as we write, this mentality is gradually changing, and some doctors are currently investigating the benefits. Over the years, the teams have multiplied, and more and more women are participating in dragon boat paddling.

This comment from a member of *Flamenco Rosa* sums up the team's feelings 'I have gained 40 kilograms of happiness'.

At the time of compiling this book, there are 15 breast cancer survivor teams scattered across Spain.

SPAIN

Cecilia Picchi of *Florence Dragon Lady* and Jan Collins of *Pink Champagne* were instrumental is bringing breast cancer paddling to Spain.

'We didn't need to speak any other language to understand what it meant.' Maxi, team captain of *Flamenco Rosa*, on the first Flower Ceremony held in Spain.

DENMARK

Denmark, a country surrounded by water, rich with the tradition of Vikings and yet, as unbelievable as it seems, until 2017, there was no dragon boating among Danes.

In the early spring of 2017, physical therapist, Kira Bloomquist PhD, called a meeting to propose establishing a breast cancer survivor team in Denmark. The *Abreast In A Boat* study conducted by Dr Don McKenzie had, in many ways, shaped her career and research regarding heavy-load resistance exercise and lymphedema risk.

Kira's expertise was the physical and psychosocial concerns faced following a cancer diagnosis and treatment. In particular, lymphedema and the role of exercise in cancer recovery. The main goal of the meeting was to establish the first Danish breast cancer survivor team to participate in the IBCPC Florence event in July 2018.

Helen Munck, diagnosed in the summer of 2016, shares, 'I attended the meeting, and there was no doubt nor hesitation in my mind. YES, I am in!'

The first step was to establish *Danish Dragons Abreast* as a breast cancer dragon boat society. Kira Bloomquist, Marianne Sonnichsen, a physiotherapist with many years of experience working with patients who had undergone breast reconstructive surgery, and Flemming Simonsen, the on-water coach, trained the eager women ready to get on the water.

The indoor training began immediately, focusing on strength, cardio, stretching, and yoga, including balance and coordination. Dance classes, learning and remembering choreography to music, were introduced as great ways to practice and improve rhythm and coordination.

'It was months before we could get in a dragon boat,' remembers Helen fondly. 'As Copenhagen is by the sea (rougher water), in the northern part of the world (cold and dark winters!), the season on the water is short compared to many other countries'.

Copenhagen Dragon Boat Club offered the use of old dragon boats they had in storage. Helen vividly recalls seeing the boat for the first time, 'I was so excited to be part of this project. I took a first glance at the old Dragon, surrounded by the dark water.

My zodiac sign is Aquarius! Water is my element, but I am not keen on depths of darkness. Honestly, I was terrified and hesitated when told to take a seat. My dear friend looked straight into my eyes, grabbed my hands and assured me that everything would be fine.

I got into the boat. Paddles Up! Ready! The Dragon began gliding through the calm water. It was awesome! With my very first stroke, all of my fear disappeared in a split second. At that moment, I knew dragon boating was for me. I was now a paddler. It would change my life forever.`

Reflecting over the years since she started paddling, Helen says, 'It was a struggle to be acknowledged. Finally, the Danish Canoe and Kayak Federation took us under their wings. It was also a challenge to recruit. I guess that there are several reasons. The lack of a tradition of dragon boating is possibly one major reason. Another reason is the cost; we pay high fees for using equipment, and we have a very short season due to climate.'

When the team started, the main goal was to participate in Florence 'I believe that every new team must have felt like we did when representing our country for the first time. The pinkness is a reminder of the shared experience of breast cancer. But the sensation of being part of it makes you forget why you are there in the first place,' is how Helen summed up the collective experience of the Danish team in Florence.

On the flight back to Copenhagen, team members decided they needed to share the benefits of dragon boating for breast cancer survivors.

Danish Dragons Abreast are the only team in Denmark at the time of compiling this book. The team has a close relationship with their Swedish sisters based in Malmo.

Sammenhold og kaerlighed –
styrke vi bliver ved og ved – go go go

'Unity and love -
strength we go on and on - go go go.'

Danish Dragons Abreast team chant

'When diagnosed with lymphoedema, I was bewildered at how many different messages I heard about what you may do and not do physically. It was important to me to use my body as I did before my diagnosis and treatments. I was not into joining an ordinary gym or fitness club, so the opportunity to be part of the dragon boat team made a difference.

Fellowship and togetherness with amazing women, hard physical training and fresh air. It makes me happy, and hopefully, my team will contribute to the important message all BCS paddlers are sending to the world and to those who may suffer the same bewilderment and doubt as I did before I joined the team.'

Marie Peck, *Danish Dragons Abreast*

SWEDEN

As the Danish breast cancer dragons were getting on the water, so too, in neighbouring Sweden, was the pink dragon boat movement being fanned into life.

The introduction of breast cancer paddling in this beautiful country with ideal waters, islands and lakes that beg to welcome pink paddlers is thanks to Åke Malmberg. Inspired by the three pink teams at the European Dragon Boat Champions in Rome 2016, he asked leaders in the Swedish team, 'Why don't we have pink ladies in Sweden?' The answer was that nobody had time for it; but he was welcome to make it happen.

Working with the support of the Swedish Breast Cancer Association, Åke began recruiting breast cancer survivors to form a team, holding a meeting in February 2017 at the Malmö Canoe Club. Women came from as far afield as Örnsköldsvik in the north to Malmö in the south, and by the autumn *Pink Dragon Ladies Sweden* had started with the Malmö Canoe Club as their base.

Emilia Peetre, a founding member of the team, shares, 'To me, dragon boat paddling is the road back to life. When body and soul go through a difficult time and life falls apart in so many different ways, it feels incredibly good to gain strength from others in the same situation. Physical activity in the outdoors is in itself healing. Meeting other pink sisters gives me such joy, new energy, and strength in both body and soul, and hope for life.'

Isabella Scandurra, living in Örnsköldsvik, some 1100 km north of Malmö, originally paddled with the *Pink Dragon Ladies* until the creation *Moälvens Drakar* within the Moälvens Canoe Club in 2020.

'We started in July 2020, when we managed to buy two small festival dragon boats. And a five seated outrigger, making it possible to go on the water, regardless of how many paddlers we had.

Of the founding members, 4 of us met as we trained for the IBCPC Festival in Florence 2018. We now have 12 active members, which is an increase on the eight we had the season before. It's a slow build, and we actively work at recruiting.'

Diagnosed with metastatic breast cancer in 2019, Isabella looks at her regular visits to the cancer care clinic as an opportunity to recruit more paddlers. 'It's a win-win situation. For us, to increase team members, but also to help them help themselves leave the sickness behind, and to find an activity that is good for your body, mind, and soul.

That is why I am a 'never giving it up-dragon boater! I will paddle for life as long as I can. And then I will be either a drummer or a steer person. And when it is no longer possible to be in the boat, due to lack of treatments, increasing mets or other bad and sad things, I will cheer on the teams from the shore.

The community is fantastic. There is no time to think of diseases, but how to plan for the next session on the water, or the next activity on land. And the best thing is that my entire family also loves the dragons on water. My kids are 5 and 7, and they are most enthusiastic, but my husband fully supports me!'

There is currently one breast cancer paddler team in Sweden; the tremendous positivity that exudes from Isabella suggests growth is no doubt on the horizon.

ROMANIA

Whilst the world went into COVID-19 lockdown, Romania, located in the Balkans, bound by the Black Sea in the south, became home to the newest breast cancer paddling team.

Cosmina Grigore, diagnosed in 2013 at the age of 27, had established the Imunis Association dedicated to educating and empowering cancer patients to rewrite their stories post-cancer diagnosis.

Marian Baban, world champion Romanian sprint canoeist and Olympian, became aware of the breast cancer paddlers through his brother Gino. The latter coached the Belfast survivor team *Lagan Dragons*. Marian excitedly approached Cosmina with a project plan to establish a breast cancer paddler dragon boat program in Bucharest.

'The reason why I wanted to create this for the first time in Romania was that patients deserve better,' said Cosmina. 'I am a mentality changer who believes that life must be experimented with to its fullest. Moreover, being a cancer thriver myself, I know how important sport is for building the needed lifestyle post-diagnosis.'

Developing the project whilst the world was in lockdown meant using online technology. Meetings between Marian and Cosmina, as well as patients keen to be involved, took place online. Zoom was their friend.

Finally, the day arrived, restrictions imposed by lockdown were lifted. The eagerly awaited first training took place on Vidraru Lake in June 2020. It meant working in line with all conditions imposed by COVID-19.

There was no dragon boat. Instead, a combination of kayaks and canoes offered the team a chance to paddle. In October 2020, *Imunis Dragons* were officially launched and were fortunate to receive a donation to purchase a dragon boat.

'After surgeries and treatment, I felt like life stopped. I felt like I had this huge tag on my forehead, and I could never be someone without the diagnosis. When I found out about the project, I signed up wholeheartedly, feeling like a little child receiving the biggest toy. This project truly brings together usefulness and joy,' are the words team member Adania uses to describe her experience. 'Being part of a group, sharing the objective and all emotions and feelings, working out together, motivating one another and, why not, being relaxed together, is just perfect for me.'

Cosmina sums up her motivation to embrace dragon boating, 'I have understood the substantial benefits this sport generated for breast cancer survivors. I find it amazing how motivating and exciting this activity is for these women. They feel stronger, lighter, beautiful builders of something that pushes them further and further. It expands them, helps them grow, makes them laugh, and brings them together in a way no other sport or activity does. I love to see patients like this. It is what generated healing: body and soul. It motivates us to continue.'

At the time of writing of this book, Romania has one team of 25 breast cancer paddling members under the banner of *Imunis Dragons* training twice a week in Bucharest.

‘ *When I started to train, I was feeling alone, not understood by anyone, useless... Now, being a part of this amazing group and feeling like someone who helps build this team, I feel like I have grown wings to fly!* ’

Mihaela A, *Imunis Dragons, Romania*

CYPRUS

Nestled in the east of the Mediterranean Sea sits the island of Cyprus with a climate and conditions that are perfect for year-round dragon boating. The sport made its debut on the island in 2008, yet it was not until 2017 that the seed for breast cancer padding began to grow.

Maria Mittiadous, diagnosed with breast cancer in 2015, unaware of the global movement of breast cancer paddlers, joined *Cyprus Mouflons PaddleSports* in 2017. 'I was the first breast cancer survivor in the club. I joined the practice sessions with great enthusiasm and loved it!'

When the team manager mentioned the subject of survivor paddlers, Maria decided to do some research. 'When I realised how beneficial the sport is, I contacted the President of Europa Donna Cyprus to organise an awareness event with the aim to inform breast cancer survivors on the importance of team exercise as well as to exchange information.' Europa Donna

Cyprus embraced the concept of possibly encouraging other women to join the sport and create a pink team.

In April 2018, the Cyprus Federation of Dragon Boat organised the 10th International Dragon Boat Festival in Limassol. 'With the arrival of the *International Pink Sisters,* the first BCS team to visit the island, we had the amazing opportunity to invite members of Europa Donna to experience the thrill of paddling for the first time. It was an opportunity to create our own team, *Pink Mouflons.*'

The team is named *Mouflon* after the local wild goat found in the mountains of Cyprus and it is a national symbol. At the time of writing, *Pink Mouflons* are a 10-member breast cancer paddling team with the objective of promoting awareness of the benefits of the dragon boat program for those post breast cancer treatment.

TURKEY

Straddling two continents of Asia and Europe sits the city of Istanbul, birthplace of *Pembe Lotus*, or *Pink Lotus*, Turkey's first breast cancer dragon boat team established in 2013.

The driving force behind *Pembe Lotus* was Cengiz Unutmaz. His interest in creating a team began when his girlfriend was diagnosed with breast cancer—dedicated to the concept of good health through proper diet and exercise for everyone. Cengiz consulted the American College of Sports Medicine about dragon boat paddling and, using the work of Dr Don McKenzie, together with the College's fitness programme, won the support of the medical profession in Istanbul.

Jenny Yule, *Abreast In A Boat*, recalls visiting Istanbul. 'Despite my not understanding a word of Turkish, it was easy to capture the absolute joy and enthusiasm of the team. With

the happy chatter of the paddlers and the coach's commands, we glided out onto the waters of the Golden Horn against the famous backdrop of the Blue Mosque, Hagia Sophia and the Topkapi Palace. As the sun set into a magnificent red, the calls to prayer resonated around the Golden Horn. The experience can only be described as magical.'

To meet the training needs of paddlers who lived in different parts of Istanbul on different continents, Cengiz arranged two training centres – an oncology clinic on the European side and the other in a private club across the Bosphorus on the Asian side.

When writing this book, we have been unable to ascertain what became of the Turkish team. Yet, we feel it is essential to record that there was indeed a group paddling in Istanbul as far back as 2013.

ISRAEL

Faced with conflict throughout history, regarded as the Holy Land by Christians, Muslims and Jews alike—the sport of dragon boating for breast cancer survivors in Israel includes all religions.

Mike Haslam, from the IDBF, shared that there had been enquiries about establishing dragon boating in Israel since 2002. However, it was not until Debbie Halton-Weiss and six other Jewish women from Ottawa and Toronto, Canada, purchased six dragon boats for Israel that the sport was finally introduced in 2012.

Among the six women was Frances Halperin of *Dragons Abreast Toronto*. Volunteers included the original owners of Great White North, Frances and Barb Goldberg. The delegation to Israel also consisted of the best coaches and steers charged with training Israeli's into the roles.

Debbie shared their motivation. 'We wanted to introduce the sport to Israel, bring the values that dragon boating fosters, such as inclusivity and diversity, and that everyone is welcome in the boat.

We introduced the sport by creating the first International Festival in 2012 to bring people to Israel, again promoting those same values. We also wanted a strong presence of BCS teams. Frances Halperin was instrumental in getting 8 BCS teams from Canada and beyond to attend that first festival.'

Participating in breast cancer paddling teams were *Canadian Abreast Heart, Canadians Abreast Spirit, Canadians Abreast Spitfires, International Pink Sisters, Island Breaststrokers, Two Abreast, Israeli Cancer Association,* and the Israeli *Yad La Hachlamah Cancer Association.* Other teams included Arabs, Jews, Christians, Druze, and Bedouins in the boat together. Many would never have otherwise been in the same room, never mind a boat.

The 2012 Festival held at Lake Kinneret (the Sea of Galilee) was the debut of the first Israeli breast cancer survivor community - *Hatira L'chaim.*

Once the Festival was over, *Hatira L'chaim* was forced to stop paddling on the Kishon River as the high levels of pollution in the water had a negative physical effect on the paddlers.

In 2018 Coach Reuven (Ravik) Ram, together with Orit Ziv established *Pink Lionesses Israel,* an organisation dedicated to breast cancer survivor paddling,

Orit, diagnosed in 2017 with breast cancer, shared that in Israel, 5,500 women discover they have the disease every year. There have been about 100,000 women diagnosed in the last twenty years, almost one in five women!!! Jewish, Arab, Muslim, Christian, Circassian and Druze.

'The medical treatment given to us in Israel is first class and one of the best in the world.' said Orit, 'However, post-treatment, there are hardly any agencies offering aftercare for women who have undergone physical and mental trauma.

When I posted a message on the cancer patient's website, within 72 hours, 60 women had registered interest in forming a dragon boat group.'

ISRAEL

Today, paddlers from across the country all paddle on Lake Kinneret (The Sea of Galilee). As Orit says, 'this is challenging as paddlers live all over Israel. It can take up to 2.5 hours travel time each way.'

Pink Lionesses Israel consists of both survivors and supporter volunteers who act as steers, coaches, and logistic managers. Many of the supporters are spouses making the dragon boating activities fun for the entire family. The organisational structure also includes a social worker and doctor to ensure the mental health and wellbeing of the members.

'I say I am just a coach,' is how Reuven (Ravik) Ram, one of the first coaches to be trained in the initial visit to Israel, describes himself. 'But some ladies have told me that I saved their lives. This group is what is saving lives. Not only because of the exercising but because of the socialising aspect.'

Orit proudly shares, 'We reached one hundred members in 2019. Women from all over the country between the ages of 20 and 80. Jewish and Arab. Both friends and sisters!' At the time of writing this book, *Pink Lionesses* has 200 women involved across four crews, including Arab Muslims, Arab Christians, Ethiopians, Jews, Russians and Druze.

Pink Lionesses is currently working to establish a crew on the Yarkon River, Tel Aviv, certified as a safe place to paddle.

The most beautiful thing is the sisterhood. The care and affection between the paddlers from all religions and walks of life.

We love and respect each other; this group is an example of co-existence. I am certain that if women led the world everything would be easier.

Orit Ziv, *Pink Lionesses* Israel

QATAR

With its capital Doha, Qatar sits on the northeastern coast of the Arabian Peninsula. It is home to the *Doha Wireless Warriors*.

Sandee Thompson started paddling in 2010 with *Bosom Buddies*, Nova Scotia, Canada. As a side effect of Tamoxifen, a blood clot in her leg, made her decide it was time to have a change of pace. Her marriage had broken up ten months before her diagnosis giving her the freedom to seek a new life. Packing her bags, Sandee moved halfway across the world to take up a position as an English teacher.

When Sandee arrived, there were no dragon boats in Qatar, 'Jeff Ching brought a dragon boat into Qatar and advertised for paddlers. We were called the *Doha Dragons*. He and I and another gal, SueAnn, taught ourselves to coach and steer.'

A year later, after a re-diagnosis of breast cancer, Sandee set a goal to establish dragon boating for cancer survivors. It was a huge challenge and a struggle to connect with survivors. 'Our survivors are all types of cancer and supporters. People come and go constantly. It is the nature of Qatar.'

Through sheer persistence, the *Doha Wireless Warriors* thrives. Sandee has built community, shared her love of the sport and helped breast cancer and other survivors enjoy the joys of paddling.

When asked how the team's name came about, Sandee explained, '*Doha* to help people find us. *Wire* because all wire bras hurt like hell after my initial lumpectomy, less after a bilateral mastectomy. *Warriors* because we all battle the beast and because Amazon Warriors used to cut off one breast to make shooting their bow and arrows easier and more accurate.'

The team in Doha acknowledges Dr Don McKenzie in their promotional PowerPoint presentation to interested paddlers. They are known as a community team where all cancer survivors and patients are welcome. Sandee explained, 'There really aren't any cancer support groups in Qatar. The Qatar Cancer Society focuses on information rather than support.'

UNITED ARAB EMIRATES

The largest of the Emirate states, Abu Dhabi, is home to the *Abu Dhabi Jets* dragon boat team.

Originally from Ontario, Canada, Jennifer Cruickshank spent 26 years as an expatriate with her pilot husband. Whilst living in Singapore for 18 years, she was introduced to dragon boating. On moving to Abu Dhabi, she started a group that brought together all the spouses of Etihad Airways.

'Initially, the dragon boat team was for this group,' explained Jennifer. 'It became so popular that we created the *Jets* encompassing the whole community of Abu Dhabi. Some of the women in the boat were survivors, so we decided to create a voice for breast cancer awareness. The team paddles to raise awareness for breast cancer in the UAE.'

With the transient nature of the population in Abu Dhabi, the team fluctuates in numbers with women from around the world, representing many countries.

Speaking at hospitals in Abu Dhabi, team members do a great deal to raise breast cancer awareness. As Jennifer explained, 'It's not like in Canada, raising awareness in Abu Dhabi is sharing that it's okay to talk about breast cancer.'

Founded in 2014, the *Jets* remain the only women's team in Abu Dhabi. Each October, they celebrate breast cancer awareness month alongside women worldwide in a celebration that includes holding a flower ceremony.

Although neither Qatar nor Abu Dhabi has an entire breast cancer team, we have chosen to include them in this book from a global snapshot perspective; it is vital to record that the movement is gaining momentum in this region.

My background is in aviation, but the naming of the team was a collective process where everyone was thinking.

We needed something that would be quick. Hence the Abu Dhabi Jets.

Jennifer Cruickshank, Founder *Abu Dhabi Jets*

CHINA

Traditionally, dragon boat has been a sport for men in China and Asia; younger men, rather than women, let alone women with breast cancer.

As a result of the appearance of breast cancer teams at the Rome World Club Crew Championships in 2002, breast cancer teams received an invitation to the IDBF World Championships in Shanghai. The SARS epidemic meant rescheduling the event to 2004.

Five breast cancer teams participated in this event – one from Singapore and one from China plus three composite breast cancer crews of *Internationally Abreast* – Hope, Inspiration, and Spirit. Michelle Hanton coordinated the Australian and New Zealand members, Eleanor Nielsen, the Canadian and U.S. members.

Unlike the elite teams, we were a group of women whose place in Shanghai was assured—we did not have to win the rights to represent our country. We had received a special invitation to Shanghai simply because we were breast cancer survivors. The IDBF, recognising competition was not our focus, delighted in supporting our cause. They provided an international, high-profile platform where we could promote our message of breast cancer awareness through the sport of dragon boat racing.

Being closely involved with establishing the breast cancer paddling movement in both Canada and Australia, we recognised the unique opportunity to promote our global message. We also understood the responsibility of representing our country and breast cancer dragon boating.

China was a whole new world and, without a doubt, very different to the West. We needed to be sensitive to the cultural and traditional aspects. We believed, working inclusively on an international basis would be more effective in promoting our message. Together we would be more likely to achieve our aim of meeting and talking with people involved in the care and support of women with breast cancer in China.

We envisaged a joint representation in Shanghai at official functions, media conferences, and other functions. We wrote to other survivor teams attending to invite them to be part of a shared broader collaboration. We knew we had an excellent opportunity to utilise our combined strength to benefit those who had travelled and those who were travelling the road with breast cancer.

Our representation at functions and public appearances could potentially create breast cancer awareness in a country that traditionally did not speak openly about any cancer diagnosis—let alone breast cancer. It was a chance in a lifetime.

Combating the logistics of language and the importance of explaining what the breast cancer survivor teams were about was solved by creating a flyer before leaving Australia. Explaining the mission of *Internationally Abreast,* translated into Mandarin, and several copies made for each team member.

The flyer read. 'We are groups of breast cancer survivors from around the world. We are very honoured to be invited to participate in the prestigious 2003 World Dragon Boat Championships in Shanghai. Whilst we have raced dragon boats in Europe, America, Canada, Australia and New Zealand, it is a dream come true to be allowed to race in China. This is the land where dragon boating originated, and we welcome the opportunity to experience Chinese culture first-hand.

Breast cancer survivor dragon boating began in Vancouver, Canada, in 1996. Lymphedema, a poorly understood side effect of breast cancer treatment, was thought to be caused by strenuous, repetitive upper body exercise.

A sports medicine specialist, Dr Don McKenzie, questioned this and recruited a crew of women who underwent carefully monitored training. From this small beginning, a worldwide dragon boat movement was started. There are now over 40 teams of breast cancer survivors worldwide engaged in active training, practice, and competition. Through the sport of dragon boating, these women have helped to change the view of breast cancer as a death sentence.

Internationally Abreast is a melting pot of women from a variety of backgrounds, age ranges and paddling abilities. We participated in Rome in 2002 and Toronto in 2001. Crew members from many countries will meet for the first time in Shanghai.

The common thread is the experience of breast cancer. We share a passionate desire to assist women diagnosed with breast cancer, to raise awareness of life after breast cancer and to work towards a world without breast cancer. We are truly 'all in the same boat'.

'Arriving in China,' Eleanor recalls, 'We were excited to be met by a Chinese team of women with breast cancer. Translators helped to facilitate conversations.

We cheered the Chinese team on the first day of races as they marched in pairs to their boat. By the time the Flower Ceremony took place on the last day of races, the Chinese team were hugging us, crying and sharing in the joy of paddling a dragon boat.'

One highlight of the trip was when Eleanor Nielsen, Susan Hartley, Josette Poliquin, Michelle Hanton and Susan Tulley attended a reception at the Shanghai Cancer Recovery Centre. It was a privilege to be treated as honoured guests, address the group on breast cancer day internationally, albeit through interpreters generously provided by the Canadian Embassy in Shanghai. A Chinese television documentary crew captured a formal exchange of Canadian, Australian, and Chinese flags, interviews, and speeches.

Seeing the changing facial expressions of those who read the translated flyers as they came to understand what the team was representing was humbling. It is uncommon in China for women to paddle. Everyone the team met from Shanghai to Xian, home of the famous Terracotta Warriors, to Beijing and beyond, displayed the same reaction.

'Whilst in China, I was interviewed by local sportswriters. They were intrigued that a woman of my age paddled! When they found out I was a breast cancer survivor, they sent women newspaper staff to talk to me. Soon I was bombarded with questions regarding my health and attitude toward exercising after treatment.'

Takako 'TK' Kimura, *Los Angeles Pink Dragons*

SINGAPORE

The island nation of Singapore was the first South-East Asian country to form a breast cancer dragon boat team. Angelina Ong, Director of the Breast Cancer Foundation of Singapore, was responsible for creating the dragon boat program for survivors, which runs as part of their Healing Through The Arts Program.

Paddlers in the Pink officially launched in January 2003. The team boats carry the message, 'Early Detection Saves Lives, Saves Breasts!' and a tag line 'We Can, We dare, We Live it! BCF *Paddlers in the Pink Rock!*'

Singapore, under the banner of IPPC, hosted the first-ever Breast Cancer Survivor Dragon Boat World Championship in September 2006.

MALAYSIA

In Malaysia, Wong Mee Yee, diagnosed with breast cancer in 2002, founded Kuala Lumpur's breast cancer dragon boat team, *Pink Challengers*, in 2005.

Wong said, 'It was at a dragon boat festival in Penang that I came to know this sport. I was so inspired to witness a team of rowers in their 60s working hard and cheering after they completed the race. If they could do it, so could I.'

Adelaide Survivors Abreast, from South Australia, played a significant role in establishing the Malaysian team. Her Excellency Penny Williams, High Commissioner to Malaysia, at a reception in 2007, said, 'The efforts of Adelaide Survivors to promote breast cancer awareness led to the formation of the *Pink Challengers of KL*, who themselves have inspired other survivors to take up this exciting sport. The teams do a great service to Malaysian and Australian communities in raising awareness about breast cancer. They make a real difference to the lives of many others in both countries.'

Pink Challengers operates under the Breast Cancer Welfare Association of Malaysia.

' *The sport has taught me one thing: Never let cancer stop you from living life to the fullest.* '

Wong Mee Yee, *Pink Challengers, Malaysia*

HONG KONG

Kathryn Lynch, a dragon boater from Canada, is credited with establishing *Dragons Abreast Hong Kong* in 2006. Dr Polly Cheung, a breast surgeon and part of the Hong Kong Breast Cancer Foundation, on hearing of the work of Dr Don McKenzie, approached her patients with the idea of forming a team.

Mingi Pither, one of the patients, explained, 'I had been dragon boating for a few years before being diagnosed with breast cancer. When I heard of the plan, I joined up and became the first Chairperson of *Dragons Abreast Hong Kong*.'

The landmark study by Dr Don McKenzie with *Abreast In A Boat* is shared annually as part of the recruitment drives conducted by *Dragons Abreast Hong Kong*.

TAIWAN

In 2011, Taiwan formed their first and only breast cancer dragon boat team, *Hsin Huai Dragon* Boat Team.

PHILLIPINES

In the Philippines, *Pink Paddlers Cebu* are a formative team yet to get on the water. However, we felt it essential to mention their fledgling team as part of the 25 years of breast cancer paddling across the globe.

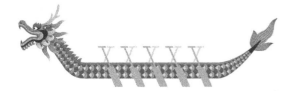

SOUTH AFRICA

At the southern tip of Africa, between the South Atlantic and Indian Oceans, sits South Africa. Beautiful Cape Town, overlooked by Table Mountain, is the birthplace of the first breast cancer survivor team in Africa.

For many years, Pam Newby, an international competitive dragon boat paddler, was motivated to start the team after being asked to helm for a group of women having an absolute ball. On finding out the women were a Canadian breast cancer survivor team, she promised to create a team in Cape Town.

It was not easy, but as the old saying goes, 'Try, try and try again.' On her third attempt, Pam was successful. *AmaBele Belles* founded in 2006, takes its name comes from the Xhosa 'Amabele', which means breast.

A founding member, Eileen van Helden, shares, 'This wonderful sport in Cape Town is even more special because we get to paddle in the Waterfront. One of the most beautiful harbours in the world, with Table Mountain as our backdrop.

I was diagnosed in 2004 and spent most of 2005 having the whole treatment menu, so after a year of being a patient, I felt tired and disenchanted. I heard about a new team of breast cancer survivors being put together for a sport called dragon boating, and I joined immediately. Only six months after we started, the Belles went to a BCS International in Singapore in September 2006. We had the most wonderful trip, meeting teams from Canada, Australia, Italy, and the UK. We even won a silver medal!

Dragon boating and going to Singapore was a life-changing experience. From the moment I first plunged my paddle into the water, I was hooked. The sheer physicality of the sport, the mood-lifting effect of the endorphins. The friendship, support, and camaraderie on the boat.'

Lenora Hammond, diagnosed in 2010, a mere six months after donating a kidney to her son, shares, 'As if in a whirlwind, I underwent a double mastectomy, followed by chemotherapy. Sadly, three out of the ten glands tested were already positive.

I was introduced to the *AmaBele Belles* and joined as soon as I finished my chemo treatments. It was love at first try…...and I never looked back. I found it incredibly inspiring to be literally and figuratively on the same boat with so many other ladies. Our journeys, experiences, emotions and even treatments all differ. Still, we share a common goal – that of living a vibrant life after Breast Cancer.'

Despite no longer being able to paddle, Lenora has positive memories of paddling. She says, 'I am enormously grateful I have had the chance to paddle for ten years. Grateful to be a part of a global movement to improve the lives of women living with Breast Cancer. My disease has now metastasised to my bones, affecting primarily my hips but also my spine and femur. So unhappily and very tearfully, I have had to give up my beloved sport.'

Living in Cape Town, South Africa, means connecting with other breast cancer survivor teams requires travel. Taking pride in showcasing the colours and vibrancy of their African homeland, *AmaBele Belles* dresses for parades at international events in colourful headscarves, skirts and face paint. They also share the songs of South Africa, including Shosholoza, Nkosi Sikelel, and Afrika.

LATIN AMERICA

Kim Bonomo, Chair of the IBCPC Festival held in Sarasota 2014 and Argentina born Adriana Bartoli, has been the driving force behind the establishment of breast cancer dragon boat teams through an outreach program to Latin America.

'I touched the sky with my hands as soon as I joined *Abreast In A Boat Deas Divas*, feeling the joy, love and energy of the team.' Adriana, IBCPC Latin America Representative (2016-2020), described her motivation. 'Probably because my homeland is in Argentina, also knowing that so many ladies could be blessed with the sisterhood, camaraderie, and love of breast cancer dragon boat paddling. I was deeply moved to share the message of hope in these lands by encouraging breast cancer survivors to embrace dragon boat paddling.'

Adriana had started working with survivors in South America as early as 2013. She jumped at the opportunity to accept the role as the first IBCPC representative for the continent, 'I had this inner engine to take hope to these lands. It is something I carry inside me.'

Kim recalls.'When we started developing the first BCS team in Latin America, we had hoped to plant a seed. A seed that would grow into a strong tree and sprout other teams around South and Central America. We are thrilled with the fact that a virtual forest has grown and is still growing there.'

Thanks to amazingly generous financial and in-kind support from the local community in Florida, surplus funds from the Sarasota Festival were available. Kim, who occupied the role of IBCPC Director of New Team Development (2014 - 2020), shared 'The thought that surplus monies from Sarasota contributed to this project in Latin America makes me personally very proud.

It was so gratifying to be part of something that is much bigger than yourself.'

Challenges included the fact that mainstream dragon boating did not exist in Latin American countries. There were no boats, no coaches and no steers. Kim quickly realised that to be successful, they needed to engage a breast cancer catalyst on the ground in each country to coordinate and carry on after the outreach team had left.

The first team was formed in La Plata, Argentina, in 2014. In the words of Mabel Toso of *Rosa Fenix Patagonia*, Argentina, 'The dragon boat awakens the lethargy in us. It shows us that, more important than the result of any dragon boat regatta (race), is going arm in arm and supporting our sisters as a team. Above and beyond the dragon boat is the realisation that BCS survivors are one in the boat, paddling together, supporting each other, respectful of our silences, sharing our happiness. We are not the same after crossing through the storm of our cancer journey, but we dream that other survivors can experience the same as we are experiencing.'

In February 2016, the outreach crew arrived —Kim Bonomo from *Save Our Sisters*, Miami plus Lynn Sparling, Carol McKay, Ysa Lutz, Yoki Matthews, Cindy Conway and Adriana Bartoli from *Abreast In A Boat*.

'Until we met with these novices, I never understood how, through the camaraderie of paddling, hope replaces loneliness and fear. It can change lives forever,' shared Adriana. 'When we spoke with the women about how dragon boating links them to a worldwide sisterhood of breast cancer survivors, many were moved to tears.'

During the outreach, the newly imported dragon boats were awakened and blessed with a Chinese Ceremony in Buenos Aires and a Catholic Ceremony in Neuquén. *The Flower Ceremony* was held for the first time in South America.

Adriana fondly recollects.'Three Brazilians joined us in Buenos Aires excited and motivated to start a team in Brasilia. As we always say, one event is an opening door. The Argentina outreach opened the door to the development of breast cancer teams in Brazil.'

Brazil held their first event in October 2016, the KA ORA Festival. It was attended by the first team established in Brasilia and breast cancer paddlers from Paulo Afonso, Salvador, Sao Paolo and Santos, plus members of the new Argentine teams. It ignited the spark for the movement to spread.

Dr Don McKenzie's presence and presentation at a conference that included medical professionals was key to engaging the crucial support of the medical community. Building momentum in South America started by helping teams to consolidate and train in safe paddle techniques.

After Dr Don McKenzie's conference presentation in Santos, Cleusa Alonso, IBCPC National Representative for Brazil from 2017 – 2020, was inspired to support the development of teams in Chile. 'Our beloved country Chile is coloured pink,' is how Paula Farias, Fortale-Senos Chile summed up her experience.

'Thanks to breast cancer survivors who paddle for life and are grateful to be alive.'

Floribeth Campos de Finizio, *Pink Warriors*, Panama, explains, 'Our objective is to inspire other survivors to participate in this discipline and show that through sports you can go ahead with your life. In addition to the sports team, we have a support group – Volunteers Pink - made up of more than 50 members.'

In October 2018, another outreach took place in Cartagena de Indias, Colombia. The aim was to share hope, generate breast cancer awareness, and help establish the first Colombian team, started by Catalina Palacio, who passed away in 2019.

Ruth Ortiz Castro of *Dragon Boat Bogota* shares that Catalina's legacy lives on with 'the second Colombian team founded in September 2019 through mentoring by Catalina Palacio. This team practices at the highest altitude in the world, at 2,600 metres above sea level, in Bogota.'

The Latinoamérica en Rosa 2019 Dragon Boat Festival, held in Neuquén, Argentina, provided an opportunity for all the new teams to meet. Over 200 breast cancer paddlers bonded together through the sport of dragon boat racing and sisterhood of breast cancer.

Today, more than 21 teams in Latin America share the benefit of the sport, the sisterhood, and the mission of generating breast cancer awareness.

FIJI

Fiji, surrounded by the beautiful waters of the Pacific, makes an ideal location for dragon boat racing. Fijian born Dolly Devi, diagnosed with breast cancer in 2016, introduced dragon boating to the island paradise in 2020.

Living in Vancouver, Canada, at the time of her diagnosis in 2016, which came just two months after her father's death, Dolly credits joining *Abreast In A Boat* in 2018 as 'changing my life forever. It combined my inherent love of water sport with healthy physical conditioning. The community within the sport was so inspiring that I knew I had to help my Fijian sisters.

There was a deep stigma surrounding cancer in Fiji. As a woman of Fijian descent, I felt an obligation to speak out in the hope it would make it easier for other women to come forward and have mammograms.'

Dolly made four visits to Fiji dedicated to building connections, forging relationships and making presentations in Nadi and Suva. Supported by the Fiji Times, the Fiji Sun and Belinda Chan, CEO of Fiji Cancer Society, meant Fiji reached the point where they were ready for a dragon boat. 'We were able to drop some of the stigma associated with breast cancer,' said Dolly. 'It became easier to recruit survivors.'

Funds to purchase and ship dragon boats to Fiji were raised by the Fiji Canada Professional Women's Network and a personal contribution from Dolly.

In February 2020, the Bula Outreach Crew, seasoned dragon boaters from Canada, Australia, and the US, including four *Abreast In A Boat* members and Dr Don McKenzie, visited Fiji. They conducted an outreach clinic that culminated in the Nadi launch of *Fiji D Dragons* on 4 February 2020, World Cancer Day. The 'D' in the team's name symbolises 'Durga,' the Hindu female goddess of protection, strength and feminine energy. The 'D' is also the initial for Dolly's first and last name.

An emotional Dolly shared 'My grandma died of breast cancer in Nadi, my hometown, where the first dragon boat was launched. She died in 1966 at the age of 51 years. My heartfelt thanks to Dr Don McKenzie, as without him, this would not have been possible. And all the love and support from Adriana Bartoli, Kim Bonomo and Jane Frost, amazing women! It's wonderful to see women empowering other women. And very special thanks to the two brilliant coaches Roslyn Webb, Alyx Stewart and the fantastic *Bula* crew. *Vinaka Vakalevu.'*

THE SANDY SMITH GLOBAL FINALE

From the start, *Abreast In A Boat* offered guidance, support, and encouragement to others living with breast cancer, keen to embark on new adventures by embracing the dragon spirit.

Guiding newly forming teams through the somewhat choppy waters of the processes and protocols that a well-managed team needed was Sandy Smith, who had joined *Abreast In A Boat* in 1997.

Gently spoken, with a flair for communication, unwavering patience and kindness, nothing was too much trouble for Sandy. Cheerfully sharing processes, ideas and invaluable information Sandy, in her role as the first Global Liaison, was always there at the other end of the email. Willing and ready to answer the zillion questions that would pop up for newly forming teams. Sandy guided the start-up in New Zealand, Australia, Singapore and the United Kingdom.

The Ten Year Abreast Celebration of *Abreast In A Boat* saw 46 teams from Australia, Canada, Italy, New Zealand, Poland and the United States arrive in Vancouver for the event of a lifetime!

The contribution of Sandy Smith, as the first global liaison, instrumental in supporting the development of many of the teams gathered for the 10th Anniversary of *Abreast In A Boat* in 2005, was recognised with the inaugural Sandy Smith Global Race. That day would have been Sandy's 50th birthday.

The Sandy Smith Global Finale is an international symbol of remembrance. It honours those who cannot paddle or have lost their lives to the insidious disease breast cancer. It is the final paddle before the closing ceremony of major international breast cancer survivor paddling events.

Coordinating the logistics of what today looks like a seamless process was the powerhouse of tenacity and logistics, Eleanor Nielsen, Founder of *Dragons Abreast Toronto*. Spending many a sleepless night worrying about how to pull the event together, Eleanor remembers 'The Sandy Smith Global race changed from the equivalent of herding cats to efficiency. It all happened because I enlisted the help of my husband, Charles, and Marilou Kane, both master organisers. Charles introduced me to Excel spreadsheets. Marilou prepared and delivered an envelope to each team at the Festival, with the marshalling lane number for their paddler. That plus communication with each team ahead of time made all the difference. No more sleepless nights!'

All attending teams choose one member from their team, often someone with poor health. The crews are compiled of paddlers from as many countries as are participating. Participants meet for the first time as they are marshalling for the final paddle. It is a special privilege to participate in The Sandy Smith Global.

Each paddler making their way down the course in The Sandy Smith Global knows they are honoured to be carrying the dragon spirit on behalf of their team. It is truly a race against breast cancer, sending a powerful message that there is still much good living to be done.

At the conclusion of The Sandy Smith Global, all dragon boats on the water, including those from the race immediately prior, raft together, forming a flotilla. The flotilla has ranged from 12 to 24 boats joined as one.

The atmosphere is electric. Heavy. Powerful emotions emanating from the paddlers fill the air. Family members, friends, spectators, officials and media expectantly gather on the shoreline. Witnessing the breathtakingly powerful Flowers on the Water Ceremony at the end of the Sandy Smith Global is never forgotten.

Filling the 1 minute of silence is stifled escaping sobs—soft sniffles. Tears flow freely down the faces of big burly men, hardened media reporters and the paddlers themselves as each remembers those who are no longer with us.

The boats draw apart when the silence breaks, ready to paddle back to shore at the end of each wonderous festival. The sound of paddles tapping in unison against the gunwales of each dragon boat reverberates as a rhythmic sound that carries across the water—the heartbeat of the dragon spirit.

Abreast In A Boat presents each representative who has the honour of paddling in the Sandy Smith Global Finale with a commemorative pin. A lasting memento of having participated in a unique event and carrying home a permanent reminder that our race, as breast cancer paddlers, is against breast cancer, not each other. In 2018 a decision was made to drop the word Race, given there is no winner.

Sandy Smith's name is known in the breast cancer paddler world because of this iconic finale. As co-authors, we feel, in the telling of the history of the first 25 years, that it is fitting to share a little more about the person Sandy was. Her daughters, Lauren and Sarah, provide an insight into their inspirational mother.

Our mother Sandy's treatment for her initial breast cancer diagnosis had been only recently completed when we picked up and moved across Canada, from Toronto to Vancouver. We don't particularly remember

a difference in her personality at that time. After all, we were pre-teens, and preoccupied with settling into new schools and making friends. Our dad had started a new job while also returning to school, and we were all managing the chaos of a temporary living situation while our new house was being built. But despite all these challenges, our mom seemed to be fully recovered from the ordeals of diagnosis, surgery, and treatments.

Mom showed up for us one hundred and ten percent. She came to all of our practices, helped with homework, encouraged our hobbies, enthusiastically volunteered with the PTA and other events at our schools. However, reflecting back on that time, we now know that while she was still going through the motions of holding our family together, she was struggling. She was busy, but behind closed doors, our mom was withdrawn, lonely, scared, and perhaps even depressed. She was not as recovered as she pretended to be.

When we think of Mom during this time, we picture her as the personification of strength and effervescence.

How could that be? How could she have been so brave, so strong, that we didn't have any real grasp of what that word 'cancer' meant for her, and for us?

The answer is simple: she had found Abreast In A Boat.

After learning about a group of breast cancer survivors who took up dragon boating as part of a research project, our mother took a huge leap of faith. She decided to throw herself into an exciting and scary new sport and joined the new class of Abreast In A Boat rookies. She and a few dozen other women who all had experienced breast cancer shared a similar drive to move past the cancer. As she grew more and more comfortable on land and water with these women, we watched as our mom found comfort, hope, and something to be excited about. The transformation wasn't immediate, but it did come; the shadow of grief and despair slowly gave way to a determination to not only master this new sport of dragon boating, but to find joy again. Abreast In A Boat did something for our mom that our family couldn't at that time, yet we still reaped the benefits. Our mom, the Smith family cornerstone, became fearless, and confident. It radiated from her in all aspects of our lives.

To be sure, our mom was on an impossibly difficult journey. There were days she would allow us to be part of those lowest moments, whether she was trying to cope with chemo side effects or dealing with a medical appointment at which she received difficult news. But it was so rare to see anything but the strength that is now ingrained in our memories of her. We know beyond a doubt that she was shown how to find that strength—and how to accept grace or help from others —by that group of survivors with whom she paddled the waters of False Creek each Saturday morning. These are the women that proved to our mom that she could try new and exciting things, that she could be happy and healthy again.

In her second year with the team, Our mom embarked on a cross-country trip with a teammate to tell the story of Abreast In A Boat, speaking to the media and meeting with groups of breast cancer survivors in several major cities. The experience of that trip gave her incredible confidence. The following year she joined the Abreast In A Boat Board, and began the work of helping anyone who expressed interest in learning about how to start a local dragon boat team. She spent hours every week devoted to this new position. Ironically, the more time she spent on Abreast In A Boat business, the more strength and love she seemed to bring to our family.

Those new feelings of confidence and optimism cascaded onto us. Week in and week out, we would accompany her to dragon boat practices, dance alongside the group during warmup, and wave as they paddled away from the dock. We witnessed our mom regain her

physical and emotional energy. We listened as she animatedly described her experiences on the water and the magic of working in tandem to make a boat fly across the waves. Our mom's time with Abreast In A Boat showed us that we can do hard things if we take that bold first step, that we can try new things and enjoy them even if they intimidate us. More importantly, we saw our mother take pride in what her strong body was capable of, despite living with cancer. As adults, we now appreciate the significance of her modeling this to us as teenage girls.

Our mom once shared that by paddling with Abreast In A Boat, she felt like she was part of a very visual symbol of hope, especially for other women facing breast cancer. By all accounts they were, providing yet another example that a group of women working together can achieve almost anything! However, to us, it felt like Abreast In A Boat had transformed our mom into a symbol of hope for our family. She showed us how to rise after adversity, to find joy in life and in service to others. But most of all, she showed us that we can be strong, confident women, no matter what life throws our way.

Abreast In A Boat drew out the very best in our mom. Called out gifts none of us knew she had. Gave her confidence and joy and purpose. Provided her — and us — with new and supportive friends. Returned a mother we did not even know we were at risk of losing.

In some ways, Abreast In A Boat has left an impression that we feel more today than when our mom was alive. Now that we've grown and have greater perspective about our mom's journey with illness, we have also unpacked the significance of Abreast In A Boat in her life.

More than two decades after our mom started paddling, and 17 years since her death, there are still very tangible connections. We inherited the love and care of a gaggle of Paddling Aunties, some of the most fierce, joyful, and inspiring women you could ever hope to have in your life. These women lifted

'Sandy's daughter gave me my pin (for participating in the Sandy Smith Global).

She thanked me for keeping her mother's spirit alive; that was such an emotional moment for me. I still think of that whenever I look at the pin.'

Lee Massey, *Dragons Abreast Wagga Wagga*, Australia in Peterborough, Canada 2010

us up through early days of grief and wrapped around us as we stumbled into young adulthood. They showed us that we would always be a part of the larger Abreast In A Boat family; we still feel that love today.

Each time our mom brought us along to meet the women in pink on the shores of False Creek in Vancouver, she was showing us the importance of finding people with whom you can truly be yourself. People that accept you for who you are but challenge you to grow; hold you to account but have grace for days when you are weak. And most importantly, people to laugh with — a lot — and out loud. Because when you're wrapped in hot pink feather boas and dancing together, at that moment, what is there to worry about?

Initially, a symbolic trophy was attached to the race. A beautifully, exquisitely carved green jade ball that represented the world. Inside, nestled several smaller and smaller globes, reminiscent of the embrace of the dragon. The dragon that started its journey in Vancouver with *Abreast In A Boat* and spread its fire to all corners of the globe, breathing joy and life into those who took to paddling post breast cancer diagnosis.

The trophy travelled to Caloundra, Australia in 2007, presented by Paul Smith, Sandy's husband. The delicate and well-travelled jade trophy also made the trip to Peterborough, Canada, in 2010. Paul presented it alongside his and Sandy's daughters.

For Sarasota 2014, Paul commissioned a new trophy; a beautiful white bird in a sturdy blue velvet box. By this time, the original jade ball was cracking under the strain of global travel. Both trophies reside safely in Vancouver, the birthplace of the global phenomenon that is the breast cancer survivor paddling movement.

Although there are no winners in the Sandy Smith Global Finale, the holding up of the trophy, accompanied by official speeches by Sandy's family representatives, is a key part of the closing ceremony. It serves as a symbolic and highly visible reminder that the race for the breast cancer survivor teams is always against breast cancer. Each one of the participants is a winner, and every crew is *first in their lane.*

" Participating in the Sandy Smith Global Race race and Flowers on the Water was very moving. It was the cuddle I needed all the years ago when I first went through breast cancer at the age of 27. "

Bronwyn Pawley, (40 years since diagnosis)
Dragons Abreast Bribie Island, Australia
on her participation at Abreast In Australia 2007

DO YOU EVER CONTEMPLATE?

Did you ever contemplate, stop and think a while?
Of the years now past behind you, the laughter & the smiles
Reflecting on the faces drifting through the years
Some are now much fainter, some have brought us tears

The things you do, the things you share
Our lives are much like smoke
That drifts & weaves around us, like dreams before you woke
People, places, names are there
They make you who you are
Families, friends & loved ones
We all have journeyed far

Tonight we're here as Pink Champagne
How blessed are we today
In Seville together, to paddle hard & play

Two silver medals for the team, here & those at home
But let's reflect on those we love, who sadly now have gone
On those who'd love to be here, paddling, racing too
For those who simply loved us & shared their lives with you

Raise a glass, hold a smile, for standing by your chairs
Are all those who you thought had gone
Each one of them is there.

Hilary Bracken - *Pink Champagne,* Bournemouth, UK

Remembrances

No one likes to give thanks to the disease that brought so many people around the world this incredible experience. But without breast cancer, it is unlikely that most of us would have ever stopped, revaluated our lives and embarked on the adventures dragon boating has provided.

It is not all fair weather paddling. In the early days, most teams were unprepared to deal with recurrences in paddlers or sometimes the death of a member. It is unsettling to be brought face to face with our mortality—it could easily have been us.

Realising how unprepared most teams were to deal with such losses *Dragons Abreast Toronto* decided to include a workshop at the 2001 Conference in Toronto to specifically cover the sensitive topic of loss and remembrance. Led by Doug Graydon, an Anglican priest who had worked with HIV/AIDS patients, the workshop profoundly affected both the 50 attendees and its presenter.

As we came to put this book together, Eleanor Nielsen shared with Doug via a note in his mailbox what we were planning. The response received is a powerful testament to the impact we, the breast cancer paddlers, had on him.

'It remains one of my dearest memories of a successful teaching event—my wee bits of wisdom relating to grief and loss, learning events as regards the wisdom I experienced from women who embraced their loss with courage and finally—how to party, with wine and music dancing on a boat in the Toronto Harbour!

I wondered how I could meet your group's needs as these experiences were completely foreign and, to a large degree, inaccessible to me. I learned quickly how generous you were.

You wanted me to know as best I could what breast cancer meant to women and how many felt so abandoned by the healthcare industry as far as recovery, loss, grief and, more importantly, the devastation experienced as regards the loss of a woman's self-image.'

Doug shared. 'I recall meeting the group—their clear expression of their experiences—each person carrying their own journey of grief. I learned how tough they all were; how far they had travelled. How much energy it took to step out and into the dragon boat community. There was to be no simplistic or shallow presentation of the in's and outs of grief and loss. The group wanted to, as is said, 'dive deep' into the topic. They wanted to see their experience reflected in the material I presented. And so, this is why I remember the day so well.

Rarely am I challenged to travel more deeply into the dynamics of grief and loss. Most people seek simple answers—easy steps to pass through the experience. Not the dragon boat ladies. They were prepared to work with me. It was great!'

Rituals allow us to act out our feelings, define our grief, legitimize the expression of emotion and bear witness to our connection with the deceased. Teams and family members alike find comfort and healing in rituals. Doug Graydon's workshop inspired participants to think more deeply about remembering their teammates.

'We came home thinking, what could we do to remember paddlers we had lost? We walked every inch of the shores of False Creek, the waterway in Vancouver where this breast cancer dragon boat paddling started.' shares Jane Frost. 'We thought about placing a bench there. We thought about public art. We pictured a series of bronzed dragon boat seats with paddlers in all the seats but one. Then reality set in. There were no bench sites left in False Creek. The cost of an interactive statue was prohibitive. The approval process for public art was overwhelming.

We wandered back to Alder Bay in False Creek, where we launch our boats. And we realised that right there was the perfect spot for a Legacy Garden. It was the grassy knoll overlooking our dock. It even had fuchsia rhododendrons in the spring. With the support of the Vancouver Parks Board, we were able to place a plaque in 'our' garden, and to this day, the garden continues to sprout pink and fuchsia flowers.'

On the opposite side of the country, *Dragons Abreast Toronto* remembers friends with a memorial bench in Sunnyside Park. The inscription reads 'Wild Women Strong and Free, Missing our Friends, Dragons Abreast.'

In Dublin, Ireland, *Plurabelle Paddlers* to mark their 5th anniversary, unveiled a beautiful granite bench at the Grand Canal Dock in memory of teammates loved and lost, including club founder Fiona Tiernan. The simple yet powerful inscription reads 'Plurabelle Paddlers, Remembering friends we have loved and lost.'

Dragons Abreast Australia has a section on their website dedicated to 'Remembering Our Angels' with a photograph and tribute to each member lost.

Chemo Savvy, Winnipeg, has a special space within a labyrinth. When a team member dies, they place a white brick bearing the member's name in the Labyrinth.

Chestmates, Kingston, forms a paddle archway from funerals and sings the song they originated, Paddles Up, Take It Away, at a member's memorial celebration.

In the early days, *Busting with Life*, from New Zealand would light a candle at their special events for members who were no longer with them.

Planting trees, park benches, plaques and scholarships or awards are some of the ways the breast cancer survivor paddling community chooses to remember those we have lost.

I know I'm dancing with death, but I'm living life like I never have before and still finding laughter and fun. Dragon boating is all part of that.

Julie Davey-Prior, *Dragons Abreast Toronto, 2000*

INTERNATIONAL BREAST CANCER PADDLERS COMMISSION

In Shanghai 2004, Angelina Ong, President of the Breast Cancer Foundation in Singapore, floated the idea of creating an international peak body to ensure Breast Cancer Dragon Boating met certain standards at events.

Discussions centred on the value of a networking organisation to oversee the consistency of our purpose and message as the sport spread and assist new breast cancer teams in their development—the International Pink Dragon Boaters Commission (IPDBC) formed. The role would be helping and guiding new team development around the world. The name changed to International Pink Paddlers Commission (IPPC)—the precursor to the International Breast Cancer Paddlers Commission (IBCPC).

The 10 Year Celebration of *Abreast In A Boat,* marked with the first International Breast Cancer Festival held in Vancouver, presented an opportunity to discuss the future of breast cancer dragon boat padding. It was evident an international organisation run by survivors for survivors needed to be the future. The IPDBC was not survivor-led.

One of the underpinning beliefs in the formation of the IBCPC was that breast cancer teams should manage their own international events. Up to this point, breast cancer teams received invitations to participate at the international dragon boat events at the discretion of event organisers.

For close to 10 years, the International Dragon Boat Federation (IDBF) invited breast cancer teams to attend the semi-annual World Championships. IDBF then formed the World CorComs, for corporate and community teams; this was the place within IDBF for the breast cancer teams.

Internationally Abreast attended the Inaugural CorComs in Berlin in 2005. The CorComs never really took off, so IDBF invited breast cancer teams to the World Club Crews. By this time, the BCS paddler movement had grown and evolved. The feeling was that the only way breast cancer teams could determine our role and place on the international field was by organising and managing our own events.

At Abreast in Australia 2007, held in Caloundra on the beautiful Sunshine Coast, representatives from each of the forty-five teams from six countries: Australia, Canada, Hong Kong, Italy, New Zealand and the United States attended an open meeting. The outcome of the meeting was a mandate to draft a constitution and by-laws for an international organisation led by and for breast cancer paddlers.

Michelle Hanton *Dragons Abreast Australia* became the President of the interim committee consisting of Jane Frost and Jenny Yule *Abreast In A Boat*, Eleanor Nielsen *Dragons Abreast Toronto*, Mary McAvoy *Busting with Life* and Sandi Buhrmaster-Jelinski *Pink Phoenix*. The committee was entrusted with formally drafting the mission statement, setting up the constitution and by-laws, designing a logo, a website, and naming the organisation.

The growing size of international breast cancer dragon boat festivals meant that one of the critical tasks was to protect integrity. Creating an equitable bidding and selection process for hosting international festivals was the top of the agenda. Dr Don McKenzie, an experienced Canadian Olympic Committee member for the sport of canoeing, was a source of invaluable wisdom in helping navigate the way to reach decisions on the trickier aspects outside the steering committee's expertise.

The Constitution and by-laws for the International Breast Cancer Paddlers' Commission (IBCPC) were officially approved by representatives from 63 teams and seven countries at the first IBCPC festival held in Peterborough, Canada, in June 2010. The 63 teams became the founding members of IBCPC after unanimously approving all the recommendations placed before them for consideration.

Notably, this included the ratification for Canada, birthplace of the now global movement of breast cancer survivor paddlers, to be the official home of the IBCPC and for the organisation to be the representative for breast cancer teams with the IDBF.

By 2010, the format of the participatory festivals was well established, including the closing sequence with The Sandy Smith Global as the finale with a massive flower ceremony.

In the fall of 2010, the first elections for the directors of the IBCPC Steering Committee took place. Jane Frost, Canada as President, Jo Parry, Australia as Vice-President, Jenny Yule, Canada as Secretary-Treasurer, Betty Solley, the United States as Membership, Louisa Balderson, Great Britain, as Communications, Eleanor Nielsen remained as an advisory member.

As President of IBCPC, Jane Frost knew that open and transparent communication was the key to success. Paddlers at all levels needed to be informed. 'Our first newsletter was published in December 2010. I remained editor for the next 28 issues, with my last issue in March 2018. In 2011 we initiated the National Representatives program. The first three National Reps appointed were Irene Chui, Singapore, Mary McAvoy, New Zealand and Mingi Pither, Hong Kong.'

At the time of writing this book, the IBCPC consists of 250 members teams across 32 different countries.

'*I'd retired from an international company. The stress was incredible. I thought I could finally relax and have fun. Then I received my diagnosis. I remember the first time I heard I had cancer. I thought my plans of adventure were gone. I thought I would not be able to do anything physical. I thought that life would be boring. However, after learning about dragon boating for breast cancer survivors my life and lifestyle changed drastically.*

I've paddled in the canals of Venice and Amsterdam, the Sea of Galilee, the Bosphorus in Turkey and in Cyprus. I even got to ice dragon boat in Inner Mongolia.

I was not the same on the inside after seeing the sun rise and set and the moon shine from the other side of the world. That glow still burns strong in me. It proves to me that we are more alike than we are not...one paddle, one boat.'

Takako 'TK' Kimura, *Los Angeles Pink Dragons*

UNIQUE EVENTS
The Ord River Marathon, Australia

Flowing through the Kimberley region of Western Australia, the Ord River rises near Halls Creek in the Northern Territory and winds for 650 kilometres via Lake Argyle and Lake Kununurra to the Cambridge Gulf near Wyndham, the most northerly town in Western Australia.

The remote, in parts, fast-flowing river winds between steep canyons and ochre coloured rocks that have stood for millions of years. The waters are home to freshwater crocodiles. The more dangerous saltwater monsters lurk near the entrance to the sea.

The Ord River Marathon is a dragon boat paddle covering 55 kilometres from the dam wall to the township of Kununurra. It was created as a bi-annual paddle by the Kununurra Dragon Boat Club to encourage other dragon boaters to visit.

In late 2003 Alan Culbertson, then coach of *Dragons Abreast NT* suggested the team should enter. He had watched his group of paddlers grow in strength and felt that this should be their next challenge.

'Australian Story,' the acclaimed Australian Broadcast Corporation (ABC) documentary that has aired each week consistently since 1996, had already decided to make a program on *Dragons Abreast*. The river and scenery combined with breast cancer survivor paddlers would provide a unique opportunity for spectacular footage to include in the program.

On the morning of the marathon, palpable excitement filled the air as sunscreen, hats, rashies, water bottles, wax, paddles and padded seats were tossed into the back of the waiting minivan. It was still dark, with daylight gradually dawning during the drive from Kununurra township to the dam wall of Lake Argyle. This journey took about an hour. Everyone was quiet and a little anxious. Would they actually make it? Would the heat knock them out? Would they be attacked and consumed by crocodiles along the way?

As they drew closer to the dam wall, the scenery was changing. Amazingly there below was the river—the mighty Ord! Thrills ran down their spines when they worked out that the three little specs way down below were dragon boats. The boats looked like children's toys given the scale of the vista.

The van travelled down the winding road before coming to a halt at the end of the road. Voices broke through the early morning silence as the participants greeted each other. Breakfast was laid out on the tables and hungrily consumed. Then, a last-minute safety brief: 'watch for the rapids and stay in formation'. This was not a race. It was an endurance paddle where all three boats participating were required to stay together.

The first hurdle was climbing safely down the grassy embankment into the waiting boats. The next dilemma was where to look first! So much to see! Between the walls of those canyons was a step back in time—the sky was a brilliant blue, the water still and calm. The dam wall just behind—the start was literally at the foot of the dam wall—a giant concrete barrier holding back the waters of Lake Argyle.

At the call of 'Paddles Up', the crew responded in unison, snapping to attention—a bevvy of pink making history. 'Go'—the journey began—one paddle stroke at a time. The breathtakingly rugged scenery along the river was unbelievable. The Kimberley kaleidoscope of colour got stronger as the day awakened—not something easily forgotten.

It was swelteringly hot. The cool river water tingled welcomingly on hot skins as the paddlers dipped their hands and hats in the water—splashing themselves and each other during the most welcome breaks. Everyone was thankful for those hot pink rashies affording protection from the blistering sun that beat down upon the three dragon boats churning up the distance.

A standout moment during this inaugural paddle took place on one of the wider stretches of the Ord in the last section of the paddle. The film crew from *Australian Story*, producer Ben Cheshire, cameraman Quentin Davis, and soundman Dav Verecchia hired a helicopter and buzzed overhead.

The helicopter banked steeply and made several passes overhead with Quentin, leaning out the open doorway filming. The sweeps on the river battled hard to control the dragon boats, paddlers jammed their hats more firmly on their heads as the helicopter draught blew in all directions.

The finish line came into view as the boats rounded a bend in the river. The epic paddle was coming to an end. The three sweeps looked across at each other, big grins spreading across their faces as they called to their crews and urged the weary paddlers to pick up their pace.

It was like a mini race—very friendly with everyone laughing with relief that the end was only moments away. The boats surged forward as spectators, camera crews, several radio and newspaper journalists cheered from the shore.

It was an emotional day for many, and the reality of what they had accomplished meant there were more than a few without dry eyes at the end.

The *'In the Pink'* episode of *Australian Story* aired on 14 June 2004. It gave *Dragons Abreast Australia* huge exposure nationally and internationally, watched by 1.5 million people, and sold to North American and South East Asian networks. The Ord River Marathon exploded in popularity and remains today, almost 18 years later, a highlight of the dragon boat calendar with paddlers around the globe aspiring to take part at least once in a lifetime.

Within Australia, it was a catalyst for forming many new member groups under the banner of *Dragons Abreast Australia*.

When I moved back to Brisbane from Darwin at the end of 2012, I thought my dreams of paddling The Ord had ended.
In October 2016 my dream was rekindled when I was invited to be part of a 2017 crew. I didn't hesitate!

I joined the gym and a local dragon boat club to reach the necessary fitness level. It was a challenge but the Kimberley landscape was well worth the effort.

Never give up on your dream. It just might take a little longer than you expected!

Gina Bleisner, *Dragons Abreast NT*

WE'RE PINK LADIES CHANT
- ORD MARATHON

We're Pink Ladies through and through
We're an awesome paddling crew
Paddling here and paddling there
Hot pink gear we all do wear

We're Pink Ladies fit and strong
Alan coaches us along
Come on in, welcome aboard
We're paddling the Mighty Ord

Will we make it, do you ask?
Yes we will, but not so fast
Slow and steady, that's our pace
We've already won our race

We've all got something off our chest
Make sure you get your breasts checked!
We want to spread the word
And make sure we are heard

We're all getting sore, sore rears
Oh, our poor, poor derrieres
We're Pink Ladies, through and through
We're an awesome paddling crew!

THE YUKON RIVER QUEST, CANADA

Although there are no dragon boats in the Yukon, it is home to the world's longest canoe and kayak marathon race. The Yukon River Quest covers 740 km (444 miles), starting in Whitehorse and finishing in Dawson City. It runs each June, on the day of the longest sun – 'The Race to the Midnight Sun.'

In 2001, Ava Christl, a breast cancer survivor, introduced Don McKenzie's research to women with breast cancer in Whitehorse. Ava and 11 fellow survivors formed *Paddlers Abreast* to enter the 2001 river quest demonstration category for voyageur canoes despite the lack of dragon boats.

After completing this epic marathon, the breast cancer survivors of Whitehorse have entered a team every year since. Ava tells us, 'At the beginning of course, we didn't know it would be a 20-year project, but the next year we kind of looked at each other and said 'who's up to doing it again?' and it started like that.

I am no athlete, but I do this. It is not just for athletes; it's for anyone who wants to have the experience. We said right from the beginning there's room in the boat for all of us. We've held to that over all these 20 years, and I'm really proud of that.'

River of Life, a Canadian National Film Board film, written and directed by Werner Walcher followed the 2006 *Paddlers Abreast* crew. The film's release inspired other breast cancer paddlers from further afield to take up the challenge.

Joanna Chrystal, Pauline Auty, Doreen Davenport, Karen Panzer, *Dragons Abreast Toronto*; Eileen Bowlby, *Bosom Buddies*; Sylvia Rickard, *Kup Sized*; Darlene Prager, *Canadians Abreast*, along with two loyal supporters entered the Yukon River Quest in June 2007.

They adopted the slogan 'Messengers of Hope' with team shirts and caps created to fundraise and publicise their efforts. As a team, they commissioned Lynn Blaikie, a batik artist, from Whitehorse to create a limited-edition art piece that each team member purchased.

Their stamina was tested paddling around the clock under the midnight sun, stopping for only two short mandatory stops, alongside many professional and recreational paddlers from around the globe. Completing the Marathon in 69 hours and 36 minutes in the Voyageur Canoe Class, they won the 'Spirit of the North Award.'

'Messengers of Hope' raised $60,000 to purchase a mammography machine for Iqaluit, Baffin Island. Previously, women had flown to large cities in other parts of Canada for mammograms.

Taking up the challenge in 2010, *Dragons Abreast Sydney* members Deb Hirst, Wilma Kippers, Rosie O'Donnell, Liz Trenam, Ruth Turnell, Tracey Bowne, Sue McClelland, Angie Aston and Vicki McLean travelled halfway across the world from Australia to the Yukon. They completed the quest in 68 hours.

' *The healing only starts when you are done treatment. You are so actively involved in going through surgery, the chemo, the radiation, you don't have time to process it. When it is all done, it's kind of like, 'Now what? How do I heal from this?* '

Rachelle Zrall, *Paddlers Abreast, Yukon River Quest*

THE VOGALONGA, VENICE, ITALY

Venice, boasting a maritime history that stretches back through the ages, is home to the Vogalonga. An annual paddling event tracing its roots back to 1974, the Vogalonga is open to all non-motorised watercraft that can be paddled or rowed. The event is a favourite amongst breast cancer dragon boat teams ranking on the bucket list of many paddlers.

Inspired by *Pink Butterfly* from Rome taking part in the 2004 Vogalonga, the stories of an opportunity to paddle in Venice spread. Breast cancer paddlers from as far afield as Australia, Canada, South Africa, New Zealand, across Europe and the USA lining up to participate as part of a Vogalonga crew.

The non-competitive event begins from St. Mark's Basin opposite the Ducal Palace. The sound of the cannon fire signals the start. However, there is no actual start line; indeed, it would be impossible to line up the hundreds of craft entered in the event.

There is something unique and majestic about paddling the Vogalonga. The waterways are awash with colour, spectators cheering and applauding from cafes, balconies and windows. Crowds line the bridges and embankments, waving and screaming encouragement to the flotilla of paddlers.

The course covers 30 km meandering through canals, out into the open water, past the islands of Murano and Burano to finish with a paddle down the Grand Canal, ending up in St Mark's Basin. The end of the event presentation runs like a well-oiled machine—each boat helm wears a numbered bib issued by the organisers—this allows the announcer to identify each crew by name on approach. There are no winners. Every participant receives a medal and souvenir poster. These are distributed swiftly by handing plastic-wrapped bundles to each boat as they paddle past the finish platform.

It was the vision of Jane Frost, an *Abreast In A Boat Original*, that truly catapulted the survivor engagement with medical professionals. In 2009 together with *Florence Dragon Lady* and *Pink Butterfly* from Rome, a crew from *Abreast In A Boat* paddling under the name *Forza Rosa* would present a united front of strong, healthy and fit breast cancer survivors.

Team member Karen Carlberg recalls, 'Before travelling to Italy, the Forza Rosa ladies visited the Women's Club at the Italian Cultural Centre in Vancouver. One of our paddlers, a medical doctor, provided information about breast cancer. Another of our paddlers, a Canadian Italian, shared a moving story of her diagnosis at an early age and concerns about being able to conceive children. After the event, a lady approached our doctor; she talked about a lump she'd had for a long time and was afraid to go to the doctor. We were stunned that even in Vancouver, where we have access to excellent medical care, the stigma associated with breast cancer is pervasive. It was a powerful yet sad moment.'

In Italy, there was still a stigma associated with the diagnosis of breast cancer. Doctors continued to advise women treated for breast cancer to never engage in any upper body movement, let alone exercise. Women lived in fear that a breast cancer diagnosis would change their bodies, making them no longer desirable to their partners, and the relationship might end. Because of these fears, many women avoided breast exams or mentioning concerns to their doctors.

Daniele Scarpa, resident of Venice and a 1996 Olympic gold and silver medallist in Atlanta, ensured doors opened as a well connected local. A breast cancer symposium was held at the Telecom Future Centre in Venice on May 30, 2009.

The Royal Bucintoro Rowing Society, established in 1882 and AVAPO Venice, an association assisting cancer patients and their families for over 30 years, combined efforts to help form a breast cancer paddler team. *Pink Lioness* in Venice officially launched on 12 September 2009. Olympic champions Daniele Scarpa and Sandra Truccolo of Canoa Republic have supported and mentored the team from the beginning.

'   As we sat around chatting, a woman suddenly
started singing, 'Je ne Regrete Rien' by Edith Piaf.
Everyone was silent; all attention was focused on this
lady who captivated us with her beautiful, strong voice
that resonated through the large outdoor courtyard.
At the end of the song, she threw off her hat and
revealed her bald head that identified her as going
through cancer treatment. The crowd applauded and
cheered at this magnificent impromptu performance.
It must have taken every ounce of her energy to sing
so exquisitely for us. '

Karen Carlbert, *Abreast In A Boat, 'Forza Rosa 2009'*

UNLEASHING THE DRAGON

As strength and confidence return to ravaged bodies, the dragon fire begins to burn more fiercely in some breast cancer survivor paddlers. In the early days, this caused some angst. Some sports paddlers felt the breast cancer paddlers were hogging the media spotlight. Breast cancer crewmates also experienced conflict, feeling criticised for not training as hard as others in their boat.

Unleashing the dragon meant there was the danger of being burnt by the fire. Handling the smouldering embers became a challenge. Those who truly understood the purpose of the breast cancer paddling teams either successfully straddled the two distinctly different paths or chose to move on. All remain grateful to the gift provided in introducing them, post breast cancer diagnosis, to the fantastic dragon boat racing sport.

To become a sports paddler means hard training both on and off the water, stretching to your maximum capacity where winning medals and being the best in the world is the goal. For breast cancer paddlers to compete as part of highly competitive teams vying for a spot on their national rosters is a testament to the power of the dragon boat program. It has opened the doorway for those who choose to challenge themselves to the next level.

Dianne Mowatt was 48 years old at dignosis and told us. 'Having never been the least bit athletic, it came as a surprise that I grew to love this water sport. To enjoy racing was an even bigger surprise! Seeing the sunsets on Lake Ontario was secondary to the freeing feeling that came from trying to focus on the paddling technique. When I joined *Dragons Abreast Toronto* after completing surgery, chemotherapy and radiation, it was the first time I could leave all my worries on the shore.

The opportunity to paddle was incredible. I loved the team aspect of all working together. The added benefit of slowly becoming more

fit pushed me to train harder. I joined in 2004 and by 2005 also paddled with several recreational teams. I just couldn't get enough time on the water.

In the late summer of 2006, I wanted to see if I could earn a seat on the *Outer Harbour* Senior Women's team. I trained with them as well as *Dragons Abreast Toronto* until the end of 2007.

I enjoyed the fun and sisterhood of *Dragons Abreast Toronto* and the fact that anyone could paddle. I liked the philosophy of *Outer Harbour* that only the best paddlers would race; you had to earn your seat by rigorous testing and training.

Once *Outer Harbour* started training for the Club Crews in Macau, I soon realised I needed to train and practice with just them. I wanted to be in the boat and not on the shore watching.

I wanted to embrace my newfound fitness and good health. I did not want to think about breast cancer.'

Akky Mansikka, a founding member of *Dragons Abreast Toronto*, became an international Team Canada steer. 'The coach asked for volunteers, but no one answered. He then asked if anyone knew how a rudder works, and I said I did from my flying experience. Airplanes have rudders and work on the same principle. Water is just a denser medium than air. That was enough for him. I was the designated steer.

Even with coaching from one of the best steers people around, I still felt inadequate that first year of racing, but I did enjoy it. I felt I was really contributing to the team. Within a couple of years, I was completely comfortable standing up at the back of the boat. By this time, a breast cancer category was established at championships where I watched the best steers, whose methods I tried to copy.

Then in 2001, the coach of *Canada's National Dragonboat Team*, Stephen Kwok, asked me to steer Canada's women's team at the upcoming Philadelphia World Championships. He'd been watching me and thought I was one of the best female steers around. I think I might have been one of only a few female steers, if not the only one! They needed a female steer for the women's category. I agreed to join their practices and benefitted from some great coaching.

I continued with *Dragons Abreast* practices for the camaraderie and fun in a more relaxed atmosphere with breast cancer survivors like myself of various ages and abilities. We were there to have fun in a supportive environment. I knew I would always find a home with *Dragons Abreast*. Membership depends on having had breast cancer, not how well you paddle competitively.

With competitive teams, you only have a spot if you are strong, committed, and meet the fitness requirements. Practice with the National Team focused on physical strength, endurance, technique, and race strategy. After all, they were there to win. At one point, I too, had to work out to meet the minimum requirement. They wanted a fit, athletic-looking steersperson. After an exhausting and intense practice, paddlers went home. No energy left for socialising. Rest and get up early to work out in the gym and practice on the water. That is the lifestyle. No weekends off. That was the time for more intense workouts and practices.

For the 2002 World Club Crew Championships in Rome, I was again invited to steer for two of Canada's most competitive teams, the *Toronto Masters*, Canada's first senior team started by Irene Hogendoorn, a breast cancer survivor from *Dragons Abreast Toronto*, and the *Stratford Sirens*. Irene wanted more frequent and intense workouts and a more competitive team with only the best paddlers, where winning was the goal. She felt that if breast cancer

survivors won in the competitive field, it would send a stronger message about fitness after breast cancer.

The rules had changed in Rome and unlike in Philadelphia, I was now allowed to steer for as many teams as I wanted. However, my primary team was the breast cancer survivor team *Internationally Abreast*. The other teams were told if race draw conflicts existed, my priorities were clear. And that was the start of my dual career. I steered in every world championship from 2001 to 2007.

With the breast cancer regattas, the energy is very different. It is a passionate and joyous event. The shoreline is crowded with supporters and spectators. The focus is on living life to the fullest, camaraderie and empowering women to do their best, whatever that may be and living healthy lives. It's about connecting with others and sending a message; yes, we all have had breast cancer, but we are still alive and thriving no matter how old, fit, or stage of treatment we are at. We are all winners no matter where we place in the race.'

***

Janelle Gamble, diagnosed with breast cancer in 1990, 1997 and again in 2005, is today a powerful, strong, and fit woman, an IDBF Level 2 Official and a world-class sweep with 12 international campaigns under her belt as part of the *Auroras* (Australia's elite national dragon boat team).

As the inaugural Chairperson of *Dragons Abreast Australia*, she recalls. 'We modelled our infant *Dragons Abreast Australia* upon Vancouver's *Abreast in a Boat*. Participation and inclusivity were paramount, and competition outcome did not matter.

We steadily grew from infancy through the struggles of our teenage years into a fully-fledged, confident, not for profit organisation. Furthermore, we became the first breast cancer group to boast a nationwide membership, gaining credibility on the international scene.

Witnessing the establishment of IBCPC was very special to me. It makes me very proud to see where the organisation is today. The impressive work being done in building new teams through participation and loudly shouting the message across the globe that Exercise is Medicine!'

Her story illustrates the demarcation between what we do as part of a breast cancer paddling team and achieving personal paddling goals.

Janelle started paddling in 2000 when recruited as the only Queenslander to join the inaugural *Dragons Abreast Australia* team. Always up for an adventure, she agreed to participate despite being afraid of both water and sharks. Needing to learn to paddle, she contacted Dallas Piwari and Tracey Evans, founders of *Brisbane River Dragons*. After five weeks on the water, Janelle flew to Sydney to race as *Dragons Abreast* at the 2000 Australian National Dragon Boat Championships held at Penrith. Despite coming last in each race, the camaraderie of paddlers and the cheer of the crowds had Janelle hooked.

As Breast Cancer Network Australia State Representative for Queensland and as a breast cancer advocate, Janelle spoke extensively about the benefits of exercise, particularly dragon boat racing for breast cancer survivors.

As a result of Janelle's efforts, *Dragons Abreast Queensland* later changed to *Dragons Abreast Brisbane* as more breast cancer survivor paddlers sprung up across the State.

Janelle continued to work on her paddling. She says, 'I started with *Dragons Abreast* and went on to achieve every possible goal as a competitive paddler. I have been so very fortunate to have travelled the world via dragon boating, and all because of breast cancer.'

Her achievements include the highest levels of international competitions, including winning the very first *Auroras* Gold at World Titles, Tampa Bay, Florida, as the sweep in the Senior A category. After reaching this pinnacle in 2011, the finale came as Head Manager of the 300+ strong *Auroras* in the latest campaign in Thailand in 2019.

Awarded life membership of *Dragons Abreast Brisbane* and the Australian Dragon Boat Federation in 2020, Janelle has never lost sight of the roots that are the foundations of breast cancer paddler teams and will always lend a hand to local breast cancer teams, encouraging the novice to experience living life to the full despite breast cancer.

OUR SUPPORTERS PERSPECTIVE

Our supporters are of incredible importance, and it is fitting that a chapter is dedicated to highlighting the impact our breast cancer survivor teams have had on supporters, and equally importantly, the contributions supporters have brought to teams around the world.

In some areas, reaching 20 or more breast cancer members is a struggle. To overcome the challenge supporters have been included as practice and paddling members. The goal is always to be a 100% breast cancer boat and to participate in a breast cancer event at Festivals, the team must be comprised of breast cancer paddlers. The only exception to this rule has been where steering is particularly difficult, and Festival organisers will supply an experienced steersperson for the conditions. Today this is infrequent as many breast cancer steers are 'the gold standard.'

A familiar sight at all regattas attended by *Dragons Abreast Toronto*, both at home and overseas, is a smiling gentleman, usually dressed in shorts and running shoes, with a flag draped around him. He is Eleanor Nielsen, founder of *Dragons Abreast Toronto's* husband, Charles Dixon.

'Eleanor came home from Vancouver raving about this dragon boat thing. She asked me if she should start a team in Toronto, and I said 'Why not'. That was the beginning of a change in our lives – practices twice a week, frequent phone calls. People asking what it was all about and if they should join. I got pretty good at selling dragon boating for a land-based man.

I found my place on the team, once we had a team flag; I would follow the Breast Cancer dragon boats to the start line and run back waving the flag. We called it 'Running the Flag'. I met them at the finish line and led them back to the tent.

I can't count the number of wonderful ladies I have met over the past 25 years, and with too many tears of admiration, I count myself a lucky man for the awesome privilege of the experience. But in those early day's many much more muscular young men were also in admiration of these ladies, and with tears in their eyes celebrated their courage and 'Joie de vivre' by forming an honour guard with paddles raised to salute them as they landed.'

When the International Breast Cancer Paddlers Commission (IBCPC) first formed, Nick Harrison, a supporter from the UK, volunteered his services to set up and manage the website for the fledgling organisation.

Nick is Patron of *Paddlers for Life*, Windermere, UK and this is his story 'My wife, Carol, wasn't able to fulfil her wish to paddle dragon boats on Windermere in the UK.

In 2006, whilst having treatment, she was excited to talk with a founder member of *Paddlers for Life* about the development of the breast cancer team. Planning was still at an early stage, and she did not see them come to fruition except in her mind's eye. A year later, plans were further developed. In January 2008, an inaugural conference invited breast cancer survivors, family members, and health professionals who might support *Paddlers for Life* to learn its benefits.

The conference reminded me that a key element of the team's ethos was to be inclusive, inviting family members and friends to participate in paddling with the team. Being recently bereaved, I was unsure where I would fit in amongst supporters participating with their family members. Nevertheless, needing something to help keep connection with Carol's dream, I eventually took the step of attending to paddle in the team's first season in 2008.

Our paddling location on Windermere is a most beautiful setting. Carol and I had walked many of the splendid fells I could see all around from our vantage point on the beautiful waters of Windermere. Such a beautiful landscape has its own capacity to help mental healing. The paddlers around me, both survivors and supporters, were rebuilding a connection with life after a cancer diagnosis and treatment. It was wonderful to see them choose adventure and this life-affirming activity of dragon boat paddling.

Like everyone, I was welcomed into the team. In my own way, I was taking tentative steps into a new life without Carol yet still keeping a connection with her. I felt that if I could not support Carol I would try and give that support to others who had shared her experience of cancer diagnosis and treatment. In fact, I soon realised I was really supporting myself. Having always loved the outdoors and being an active person all my life I knew dragon boat paddling was one of my own steps towards renewal.

Nearly thirteen years later Carol has travelled with me in my mind as I have learned many new skills and taken on all sorts of new challenges to fundraise for the team such as abseiling, long distance open water swimming and extreme obstacle courses. I have paddled dragon boats in beautiful locations on rivers including the Thames in London for the Jubilee Pageant, Lancaster canal and Scottish Lochs and Firths with wonderful people who also rejoice in the experience.

How heart-warming to watch new paddlers who come to join us and see in their faces the joy of this activity in our beautiful location. Although sharing the common activity of dragon boat paddling, everyone who participates brings their own unique life experiences and takes from the team participation the things they need to help them heal and reconnect with a life more balanced. Little wonder that all participants relish what they experience and achieve.'

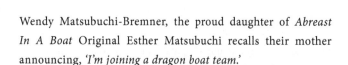

Wendy Matsubuchi-Bremner, the proud daughter of *Abreast In A Boat* Original Esther Matsubuchi recalls their mother announcing, '*I'm joining a dragon boat team.*'

'Our whole family looked at each other, wondering if we'd heard correctly. Mom was joining a dragon boat team? 'But you told us that you can't do any of your activities anymore: no piano, no gardening and no sewing, or you'll end up with lymphedema!' Matter-of-factly, Mom explained that some researchers thought that maybe this wasn't true, and that she was going to be one of the two dozen breast cancer survivors that had signed up to be part of that research study. Later, Dad remarked that Mom and the other *Originals* had risked permanent physical disability if the UBC researchers were wrong, but that if it weren't for the courage of those first paddlers, that millions of women and their families would still be prisoners of their sedentary, motionless upper bodies. Dad was always Mom's strongest supporter, even when illness eventually kept him from attending regattas.

Mom, who had made it through the World War 2 internment of Japanese Canadians, Mom who had been in Toronto's second graduating class of dental hygienists, Mom who had raised four children on three continents because of Dad's work, and now, Mom the dragon boater. Even though she previously only drove to Vancouver on special occasions, she started zipping through the downtown core at rush hour and on Saturday mornings with ease, eager to meet up with *Abreast In A Boat* team mates.

At the first regatta, I could barely contain my pride. My mom, the fuchsia shirted dragon boater! Our whole family and many friends came out to see the dragon boating newcomers.

I snapped photos from every angle, of every woman. However, at the same event, I could barely contain my anger. 'Look at those women. They think they have a chance? We'll show them!' I heard a young man jeering as his all-male teammates marshalled alongside our Originals, proudly wearing their new, 100% long sleeved cotton shirts.

In the last twenty-five years, I've heard it all, from ridicule to awe. *Abreast In A Boat* has inspired hundreds of breast cancer survivors to join dragon boats on six continents—including in cultures that previously silenced any reference to cancer.

At festivals, I always show up with my Nikon and Nepali yak bell, to cheer on my team, and snap as many action shots as I can. Most people automatically clear the way when I start ringing my bell loudly enough to summon yaks in faraway Nepal, but for those who still ask if I am official, a raised eyebrow or a flourish of the sonorous, handmade bell has always got my camera clear shots of my team. In a quarter century, I estimate that I have taken more than 100,000 'Super Snaps' of *Abreast In A Boat.*

When people learned that MY mother was Esther the *Original*, they came and took selfies at our tent or waited for her to finish eating her snack at the back of the tent. An autograph? A selfie? Please? Another amazing regatta.

For me, the icing on the cake was at the very end of the closing ceremony in Florence when Dr Don addressed the hushed crowd. In the blazing sun, after a very brief but heartfelt thank you to organizers for their three years' planning, he reminisced:

'I only have a minute, so I have to tell you a very short story, and it has to do with some of the original members of *Abreast In A Boat*. About two weeks ago, I was able to get my kayak in shape, and I went down to where the *Abreast In A Boat* team was working out in a body of water not far from where I live. I was paddling along beside the crew, and after a piece, where they had been doing some race-based work, Esther turned to me and said, 'Am I pulling my weight?'

Now, Esther has been in the boat since Day 1. This is her 22nd year, consistently paddling in *Abreast In A Boat*. And right behind her was Carol, and Carol is also an *Original* and still paddling. And adjacent, or at least nearby, was Jane Frost. So those are the three *Originals* who started this and deserve all of the applause for what they did initially, twenty-two years ago. I paddled beside them, and Esther turned to me, as I mentioned, and she said, 'Am I pulling my weight?' This is an 81-year-old paddler. And I said, 'Yes, you are. And more so.'

And then I got thinking about that. And I thought, in any other sport, in any other competition, pulling your weight simply means are you able to move and participate in making the boat go fast. In this population, it means much, much more, because pulling your weight means you understand what the slang term *'all in the same boat'* really means.

It means you have to be there for the novice paddler who's coming to you tentatively wanting to paddle, often for more reasons than just wanting to get into a dragon boat. You have to be there for the partner beside you who might get ill or sick or have problems. You have to be the world's greatest person as far as I can see. There's Esthers in every one of us. And I think that answers the question of 'Are you pulling your weight? Well, this is a pretty unique group and I'm so privileged to be part of this. Thank you for coming to Florence.'

COACHES

Coaches are a crucial ingredient in the success of any team. Just as we have an impression of our coaches, the breast cancer survivor paddlers have profoundly affected many of their coaches.

'We hear so many stories about what dragon boating does for the paddlers, the survivors, the strength that it gives those still battling cancer, the friendships, the list goes on. What we don't hear is what the coaches get out of it. Being a part of this journey has changed me. I have been through a huge spectrum of emotions. These ladies have given me a massive amount of self-respect, confidence, and pride.' Those are Graeme Rountree's words from New Zealand when asked to contribute his impressions of how, in 1998, at the age of 25, he became the coach of *Busting with Life*, Auckland.

His journey began when his mother, Trici Nelson, founder of the breast cancer survivor dragon boat movement in New Zealand, volunteered him as coach, 'Mum I'm shy and have little self-confidence.'

'As your mother,' Trici Nelson replied, 'I'm asking you to give it a go. You are the only person we know that has paddled before, come to one training. If you don't like it, that's ok, but you will come to one training.'

'When I went to that first training, I knew very little if anything about coaching but enough about how to paddle so I channelled my previous coaches and did what they did. The main difference was my previous coaches were coaching sporty people in their 20's. I learnt very quickly that this would be different and that my new team of 25 middle-aged, strong-minded women saw me as a son more than a coach.

Together we learnt along the way and grew together to become a strong team. There was no rule book; we were the first breast cancer survivor dragon boat team outside of Canada and America. Back then, the internet was new, so online resources didn't exist.

There was no set path and no point in having ridiculous expectations, so we embraced it and went with the flow. We battled through with laughter as one of our main strengths, although there were tears and a few tantrums along the way (but the ladies forgave me for these most of the time).

Busting with Life was invited to Canada as *Abreast In A Boat* guests in 2000; we attended a dinner with the Canadian team, and I got to meet and spend time with Dr Don McKenzie. What a privilege!

Fifteen years later, after coaching three breast cancer survivor teams, a high school team of girls and many open teams, I finally said, 'Mum, I think I'm done.'

'It still gives me goosebumps!'. These are the words Elaine Munro, first coach for *Dragons Abreast Toronto*, uses to describe her experiences with the team as she reflected on her experiences 20 plus years into the past. So vivid are her memories.

'I could see expressions change as team members climbed into the boat. It was like stepping through the looking glass. That became our focus mantra. Together, in our boat, we would become 'One'. Each paddler (twenty in all), drummer, and steersman represented a pulsing valve of our dragon boat 'Heart'.

Moving the boat took a bit more time. We would see other teams practising starts and doing 'hard tens'. I needed to find our paddling mantra!

I like to think that Mother Nature nudged us along. It was an early evening practice, and the lake water was as smooth as a mirror. As the paddles snapped forward to dig into the next stroke, droplets of water sprayed from the paddles, making it sound like rain.

That's it! We need to 'make the water dance'! The better the timing, the better the boat moves.

When race day finally arrived, we did a pre-race visualization. Each person imagined a cocoon of energy surrounding them, filling each cell with pure light, melting away any doubt or fear. Before they opened their eyes, they imagined a butterfly emerging from their heart in all its colourful glory. The butterfly represented their strong but delicate spirit, set free to make the water dance.

I had never yelled so hard through an entire race, as I did when the team paddled their first race and crossed the finish line. There may have been water dancing from those paddles, but there were also tears of joy rolling down our cheeks as we witnessed the *Dragons Abreast* spirit in action!

They are my *'butterfly heroes'*, reminding me of the value of teamwork and the beauty of caring for one another, on land and in a boat!'

'I came from a very competitive background as an athlete (Olympics) and coaching National teams so I took that same approach with our group' explains Fred Heese of his time coaching *Dragons Abreast Toronto* in their early years, 'I think the ladies appreciated the fact that I treated them as serious athletes and some of them continued on years later to join the National Senior teams.

We worked hard with our off-season pool program and with our dryland weight training sessions so that everyone improved. We were able to execute the proper dragon boat technique despite some residual issues from the cancer surgeries a lot of the ladies had dealt with. I was always profoundly impressed with everyone's dedication and enthusiasm and the ability to rise above personal challenges while living in the moment.

I will never forget the ladies we lost during my tenure and the profound sadness I felt when there were funerals or water ceremonies to honour our fallen comrades. I will never forget and I feel honoured to have been a part of the team's life journey.'

Fast forward to 2019 - 2021, Richard Seto had this to say of his experience 'to me, breast cancer paddling means tenacity. Every person I see step on that boat is a fighter, whether they think it or not. This person did not take their diagnosis sitting down, nor did they throw in the towel. This person did not let a diagnosis define them and tell them what they could or could not do. This person looked death in the face and told it that it was not yet their time, that they still had more work to do. As a coach, when I ask them to give one hundred per cent, I know they will give that and then some just because of the type of people they are. Each and every breast cancer paddler I know is an absolute inspiration to me; I am beyond privileged to have the opportunity to learn from 22+ role models and mentors.'

Sherri Magee, Assistant Coach, 1996 to *Abreast In A Boat,* shares 'I led the warm-ups for several years. The music was loud and fun; our favourite song was 'We Are Family'—we stretched and danced and there was lots of laughter and numerous hugs. It was always chaotic lining up and loading the boat. Still, they paddled in unison once we got on the water (most of the time!). When the coach said, 'Let it run', there was a collective sigh of accomplishment, exhaustion and camaraderie. The excitement of preparing to be in a race was palpable.

Of the history-making race day at the Alcan Festival 1997 Sherri recalls 'Diana and I were frantically running around corralling the women, lining them up, making sure they had their sunscreen, band aids, gloves, and water bottles. We were such proud parents watching our little goslings go off on their own. It was truly an overwhelming experience to watch them load in that first boat, paddle away with confidence and finish the race with power, strength and sheer joy. And on the sidelines, friends and family were lined up cheering and crying, their hearts were wide open and they were so very proud of their moms, wives, and daughters. I will never forget that feeling of sheer grace and joy.'

As we put together the final touches for this book Sherri told us, 'Twenty-seven years later I'm still in awe of these women. Their courage, their intense perseverance, and their drive to spread the message that there is an active, wonderful, fulfilling life after breast cancer. I am forever grateful to have been a part of their incredible adventure. They have enriched my life greatly, and they are some of my favourite women on the planet!'

Coach Joe Dizon had a profound effect on Pat Brown, *Dragons Abreast Toronto*, who recalls, 'It was my first year paddling and I had only been in a dragon boat for practice a couple of times. We had a wonderful coach named Joe, a short, stocky Filipino man who liked to stand on the front seat so everyone could see him while he gave instructions. I wasn't sure if I would take to the sport of dragon boating. So instead of buying myself proper rain attire, I borrowed my sister's rain slicker that she wore on their sailboat. The jacket was too large, and it had a huge hood. I looked a lot like a Nova Scotia fisherman.

We suspected rain that evening, but we did not anticipate the torrential downpour that took place when the skies opened up. The rain was pelting, and we were quite a distance from the docks. I pulled the hood up on my jacket, and because it was so large, the brim hung over my face, and rain streamed into my eyes. I hunkered down, pressing my paddle in the water, shaking with cold and fear with every stroke. That's when Joe started yelling at me.

'Push your hood back, look up at me, look up at me!' Joe shouted. 'As I threw my hood back and looked up at Joe standing with his feet straddling the width of that tiny front seat, bracing to keep his balance with the waves slapping at the sides of the boat, he flung his arms out wide, turned his face up into the rain and shouted 'Ain't it great to be alive!!'.

That's when it struck me….. In my 6th month of chemo, my body was running on empty. I had collapsed. It was touch and go, but here I was less than a year later in a dragon boat on Lake Ontario. In a torrential rainstorm. Cold and shaky, and I had never felt more alive in my life!'

Deb Middleton, an Original of *Abreast In A Boat*, shares how she became their first survivor coach.

'My first experience with cancer was when my mom was diagnosed with breast cancer. She was only 42 years old when she passed, and I was 16. I had no idea at that time how my story would unfold and how cancer would continue to impact my life. I was diagnosed at the ages of 33, 34, and 36.

After my first diagnosis, I had a new outlook on life. I didn't want to miss out on any experiences or adventures because I did not know what the future had in store for me. In 1996, just prior to my third cancer diagnosis, I was approached to participate in a study for women that had experienced breast cancer. Dr. Don McKenzie, a sports medicine physician and researcher at the University of British Columbia, launched *Abreast in a Boat* as a research project.

After joining *Abreast In A Boat*, I was unsure that it was something I wanted to be a part of long-term. I was uncertain of myself because I lacked confidence. There were not many people who had survived two breast cancer diagnoses, and I was one of the youngest members of the crew. I did not know where I fit in. After my third diagnosis, I continued to paddle throughout treatment.

Years later, I was honoured with the opportunity to become a coach for *Abreast in A Boat*. I felt it was important to pay it forward and be there for the young women who were now facing their own journey with breast cancer.

Today, I am 60 years old, appreciating every moment, blessed to be growing older, and grateful to be sharing life with family and friends. Paddling continues to be a major part of my life. I am so grateful my story continues, in large part due to a little research project that grew exponentially, forever changing the lives of so many people around the world.'

Alessandro Piccardi was instrumental in the formation of seven new breast cancer survivor teams across Italy within six years. Alessandro, former coach and team manager for the *Florentine* team at the Canottieri Comunali Firenze and the *Italian National* team, was at the 2002 World Club Crew Championships in Rome. 'I knew Orlanda because she was a drummer for the *Italian dragon boat team*. We both first came into contact with the breast cancer paddlers in 2002.'

On returning to Florence, Alessandro started to investigate establishing a breast cancer paddling team in Florence. Finally, in 2005, he managed to make the right connections and in September invited *Pink Butterfly*, established by Orlanda in Rome to provide a demonstration at the Ponte Vecchio sull'Arno.

When asked what motivated his interest, Alessandro shared, 'I was already involved with dragon boating. I had created a collaboration with the Società Canottieri Comunali Firenze where I am a member. These two ingredients meant I was well placed to see the birth of a team in Florence.

Right up until Orlanda passed away, we talked almost every evening after dinner. When Orlanda called, my daughters would say, 'Father, it is your friend from Rome.' We were focused not just on training but also on ensuring that we had medical approval for the dragon boat program. I had great satisfaction in seeing women who never thought they could have done sport have such a wonderful experience.'

A highlight for Alessandro was Peterborough in 2010 and dreaming of holding such a festival in Florence. 'After Sarasota, the dream came true for Florence in 2018.'

Diana Jespersen, Research Assistant to Dr Don McKenzie at the University of British Columbia, shares her memories of being involved both professionally and as a volunteer with the formation of *Abreast In A Boat*.

'When Don told me that we - Sherri, Don, and I - were going to put a dragon boat team together for the 1996 Festival in Vancouver, I thought, 'What fun!' We had no idea it would explode into the worldwide phenomenon it is today. Nor did I realize what an impact it would have on my position at UBC as Don's Research Assistant.

To say that the dragon boat took over my position at UBC is an understatement. In the first year, it was manageable, but going from one boat to three boats in our second year dramatically increased the workload. In addition, word was spreading to other places, and the lab phone was the go-to number for information. With teams developing elsewhere, festivals mushrooming locally and away, awareness of breast cancer dragon boating escalated, as did the impact on the Lab and my work there. We had others helping with coaching and formed a board to spread the workload, all of which helped a great deal. Still, I knew that doing dragon boat management almost full time was not sustainable in the years ahead, not if I was to keep my pay cheque from UBC.

However, right from the beginning, the thrill of helping each new paddler was such a privilege. Their enthusiasm was infectious, and the desire to get every person who wanted to participate into a boat was a great impetus to continue. The difference they were making in the world of life with breast cancer was undeniable, and who wouldn't want to be a part of that!

At our practices that first year Sherri would do the warmups, thankfully, and then we'd help load the boat(s). This was often a significant challenge, especially if you had to cross through an extra boat or two to get to yours! Lots of chatter and laughter and no one listening!

Sherri and I paddled a little, Don coached from the front, and Dr. Irve Kusck was steering. This was a flexible arrangement depending on who could come to the practices. Sometimes Sherri was coaching from the front and handed out the candies, Don was coaching and steering, and I was in my kayak critiquing alongside the boat and, apparently, known to say, 'Shut up and Paddle!'

As the years went by and paddlers were trained to be drummers and steers, our coaching took place outside the boat with Don and me in our kayaks, one on each side. It was a great way to go up

and down the boat to help each paddler with their technique or encourage a novice to take a break. The practices were always fun, even in the rain.

Festivals were especially hectic. I remember many festivals running back & forth to make sure everyone was in line and ready to paddle, only to find a few would have to go to the bathroom or had forgotten their seat cushion, or their gloves, or maybe even their paddle. All attempts to keep the herd together would be futile. And 'would you mind holding my jacket, my fanny pack (it was the 90's remember), my water bottle.' I looked like a pack mule during their races! But it was so worth it. The excitement of a group of mostly middle-aged women getting ready to compete, for the first time in many years for most of them, was so inspiring to everyone watching, especially to their families. There was no talk of cancer, or treatments, or any sad faces. Just lots of laughter and joy at being part of this special group, of being on a team, of racing, of feeling the change in their lives. It was the best!

As time went by, Don pursued his interest in exercise and breast cancer in the form of several research studies with his graduate students. This was separate from the dragon boat, which was done as volunteers and not connected to UBC. The research would all be done through UBC Research Services, ethically scrutinized, and publishable for other researchers to view. This was so important in order to get the worldwide medical community to acknowledge that the myth of strenuous exercise causing lymphedema was just that...a myth.'

FUNDRAISING & SPONSORSHIP

Launching a dragon boat group and getting onto the water requires considerable funds. Costs vary from location to location; influenced by many factors, including whether a team is taken under the wings of an existing dragon boat or canoe club where boats are readily available.

Keeping membership fees low to be accessible post breast cancer treatment for anyone keen to join is what most teams aim to do. This is often managed through sourcing start-up funding from local community groups, government grants and sponsors.

The amount of media attention generated frequently aligns with the level of funding received. In the formative years of the breast cancer paddling movement attracting sponsorship proved to be relatively easy.

Abreast In A Boat started being sponsored by Scotiabank in 1998; the bank then announced they would support a team in each of their regions across Canada. The support from Scotiabank continued for 15 years.

In 1999 *Abreast In A Boat* undertook an awareness tour across Canada made possible by the financial support of Scotiabank. 'We set up two teams with two paddlers each', explains Jane Frost. 'One of these paddlers was Sandy Smith, *Abreast In A Boat's* global liaison, and the other was Kate Doyle, an *Original.*

One team flew to Halifax and visited 4/5 cities ending up in Toronto; the other team started in Winnipeg and ended up in Victoria. The teams met with breast cancer organizations, medical personnel, Scotiabank employees and had many media interviews. It was a triumph of a trip and launched breast cancer paddling across Canada.'

Founding members of *Dragons Abreast Australia* received training in handling the media as well as consumer advocacy. Their expertise resulted in successfully generating a large amount of coverage. Media exposure ranging from print, television, and radio saw significant interest and enquiries in establishing a *Dragons Abreast* team.

Cynthia Kuiper, of *Dragons Abreast Sydney*, in the role of inaugural National Community Liaison for *Dragons Abreast Australia*, proactively researched and identified speaking opportunities within hospitals and the community. Lexie Warren of *Dragons Abreast Brisbane,* with long-term Rotary International connections and a background of understanding local service club operations, helped build relationships with service clubs. *Dragons Abreast Australia* regularly provided guest speakers for Lions, Rotary and Zonta groups across regional Australia.

The speaking engagements often led to financial support for the local *Dragons Abreast* group in their community. For the 2007 *Abreast In Australia* event, the service clubs combined to provide volunteers and financial support to ensure the 2000 attendees from across the globe experienced the event of a lifetime in Caloundra.

With this ability to raise funds and garner media attention, there comes a responsibility to use the money generated under the banner of breast cancer ethically. Policies vary between countries and between teams within countries. In most situations, this money goes to boats, mooring, coaches and costs related to practice and registration in festivals. Some cover the team uniform and other equipment. In other words, the cost of 'getting in the boat' and racing fees are covered by the team.

The significant variable is the individual members' travel costs. Some teams give members a portion of the costs of travel for use as the individual sees fit. Others consider travel costs, local or international, to be the individual's responsibility. Others put considerable effort into fundraising to cover travel and accommodation for all members. For teams whose policy is not to fund international travel, it may always be the same team members that can afford to attend international events.

Teams typically also engage in more minor fundraising activities – games nights, social events, raffles, team building outings, sale of jewellery or other products and countless other activities. Those that seek sponsorship have an equally wide range of sources. Some have corporate sponsors, others health organisations or small local businesses.

The common factor for success is an appreciation of assistance and attention to keeping a positive relationship with sponsors and donors regardless of the size of their contribution.

Sponsorship rises and falls over the years. An ideal arrangement is like a partnership. The team receives a yearly donation, and members work with the sponsoring company to assist them in their business. They help us: we support them.

Two examples of such a partnership are *Dragons Abreast Toronto's* relationship with Jones New York and Anita Canada. In 2000, the President of Jones New York, Canada, heard a couple of *Dragons Abreast Toronto* members interviewed on the radio; he promptly decided to sponsor the team. This is rare and was a great coup at that time. The partnership side of the arrangement was when Jones started their annual fashion show to support Wellspring. *Dragons Abreast Toronto* members sold tickets, modelled, collected prizes and served drinks at the event.

The second partnership with Anita Canada came from a chance meeting in the beer tent at the local *Dragon Boat Festival*. Anita was expanding their services in Canada to include the sale of breast prostheses as well as brassieres. *Dragons Abreast Toronto* members provided models for the Anita training programs for retailers on the correct way to fit women with a range of surgeries for breast cancer. Breast cancer paddling team members as models meant retailers heard directly how they preferred to be treated in the retail environment. The shared breast cancer stories created a better understanding between supplier, retail and the customer with breast cancer.

Anita also hosts a media event every year, inviting local media to attend. These have become a full day program including dragon boating with *Dragons Abreast Toronto*, lunch and an opportunity for team members to promote the benefits of the survivor dragon boat program. Beautiful Bodies and Unbreakable Spirit, Anita's high-quality coffee table book features seven Dragons Abreast Toronto members. The book is scheduled for release in fall 2021.

On hearing about this book you are currently reading, Mark Caskenette, Managing Director, Anita Canada, said, 'It sounds like a great project to spotlight an amazing organisation and sport. Everyone in the world experiencing breast cancer should know about the amazing, groundbreaking work done in Canada!'

Jane Frost of *Abreast In A Boat,* shared 'Don McKenzie, and I were in Toronto for a padding event. We visited Peter Godsoe, then Chairman of Scotiabank who showed us the bottom drawer of his desk; it was filled with thank you notes from breast cancer paddlers across Canada. He told us that he would pull out some of those letters when he was having a bad day, and they always cheered him up. One of their employees also revealed, Peter circulated those letters to his staff. They knew he had read them because he always marked anything he read with a green check mark'.

DRAGON TALES

The contributions included in this section provide insight and powerful stand-alone perspectives. They are stories of significant moments, adventures with the dragon spirit, living life to the fullest despite a breast cancer diagnosis.

TAKE IT AWAY

Suzanne Bodner, *Chestmates, Kingston, Ontario*

The words to this inspirational song were written in 2007 by Deb Schutt, a member of Kingston's *Chestmates* breast cancer dragon boat team. At about the same time, she was dealt the cruel blow of a diagnosis of Amyotrophic Lateral Sclerosis (ALS).

Take it Away!

Women of power paddling strong,

Each with a story to share.

Joined in battles -- triumphant spirit --

Always a shoulder to spare

Miracles happen when we pull together.

Dig deep, eyes ahead -- all as one!

Miracles in motion, we glide through the water,

Winners in every race run!

Paddles up! Take it away!

Paddles up! Take it away!

As we paddle on!

Take it away!

And make everyone strong

Deb's dream was that her words would one day become the lyrics of a team song that Chestmates could sing on the shores of Kingston, Ontario (Canada)'s Cataraqui River as we pulled away from the dock in our dragon boat.

Some dreams are meant to go big. And the Universe certainly backed this little one of Deb's!

Through a series of serendipitous zig-zags and ever-looping and widening spirals of jaw-dropping community support, 'Take It Away' became a beautiful CD whose message of hope, friendship, and celebration still inspires those touched with breast cancer all around the world.

Deb's lyrics were given an uplifting driving melody by a local songwriter who says that the 'Take It Away' project was sprinkled with pixie dust right from the start.

I still, to this day, marvel at how disparate Kingston community members, who had no creative connection with each other, came together in a wildly magical way to give birth to this inspiring anthem. All of the local talent was donated with a full generous heart that embraced the meaning of the song and the powerful connective impact it could have -- both as a fundraising tool for *Chestmates'* main supporter (Breast Cancer Action Kingston) and as a rallying cry for those of us who ride the dragon.

In June 2010 'Take It Away' had its global début at the International Breast Cancer Survivor Dragon Boat Festival in Peterborough, Canada; the event brought together seventy-three breast cancer crews from Canada, Australia, England, New Zealand, South Africa, and the United States.

From the first series of powerful drum beats to the final triumphant chorus, 'Take It Away' inspired us all to join together in a burst of song with paddles held high in the air. Many copies of the CD were purchased in Peterborough and taken home to become part of Pink Carnation ceremonies of both celebration and remembrance around the world.

Deb's own voice was silenced not long afterwards when several months later ALS finally claimed her life. Deb was escorted out of the church at her Celebration of Life by her *Chestmates* teammates who formed a paddle bridge and sang her song back to her in one final and collective remembrance.

I like to think her spirit still soars to the drumbeat of 'Take It Away'. Her sky-blue eyes looking down smiling at breast cancer paddlers as their steersperson encourages them to 'dig deep all as one' as they glide through the waters of rivers, lakes and seas around the globe.

ORIGINALS' INITIATING A NEW ADVENTURE

By Bunny Rosse, *Abreast In A Boat 1997* and still paddling

As paddling members of *Abreast In A Boat,* Sheila Blair and I took a team information booth to many events in Vancouver's lower mainland. It all started at a team meeting when someone said we should start an information booth to spread our message. Sheila put up her hand, saying, 'Bunny and I can do that.'

Our first booth expedition was in 1998 when we met with a breast cancer survivor group. The members were astonished to hear our story and to realize this information could change their lives. We went to trade shows; boat shows even had a dragon boat at one, conferences, malls, sporting events, drug stores and anywhere we thought we might find prospective paddlers. It was not long before groups were calling us to ask if we could attend their event. That kept us going for years.

The booth is a 3 sided, 3 foot tall black felt frame that stands on a table adorned with loads of shots of paddlers in action. Photo albums of dragon boat regattas attracted attention from many non-paddlers. All sorts of information was available, from the team, BC Cancer Agency, breast cancer groups, and newspaper clippings and magazine articles about our exploits. We always had stickers, paper, crayons and sometimes balloons for the children. We would never be without a vase of fresh flowers, usually from Sheila's garden and in our trademark fuchsia colour.

We enjoyed talking to the people who wanted to know what we were about. Those with breast cancer were comfortable talking to survivors. We tried to gently coach them into considering dragon boat paddling as a new adventure. We explained that dragon boating can be for anyone; any size, shape, athletic ability and paddling experience. After all, 'we are all in the same boat.' The idea of joining a group, getting physically active without fear of lymphedema (subject to team precautions) and becoming healthier was most appealing. People were always happy to talk to us either about their own experiences or for someone they love. Inevitably we would come away with two or three prospective paddlers from each event.

I then had the pleasure of being the *Abreast In A Boat* novice 'coach'. For many years, it was my responsibility to contact the newbie, novice or gosling as we referred to them. We gave them the name 'goslings' as our season occurs during the months when the Canadian geese give birth to their goslings. Vancouver's waterways are awash with baby goslings being herded together by their mothers. This was reminiscent of our coaches having to herd us around at regattas. One coach got so frustrated that she brought a long rope to the event and we had to all hold onto the rope while we traipsed between our tent and the marshalling tent.

Over the years Sheila and I counselled hundreds of people to join a dragon boat team and if not that, to know that regular upper body exercise is beneficial for those treated for breast cancer.

I especially remember the young paddlers. Shortly after her marriage, Anita was diagnosed with breast cancer. We paddled together on the *Abreast In A Boat* Barnet crew, one of the six crews that made up the team. Her favourite fundraising event was 'The Weekend to End Breast Cancer. Her magical personality inspired us. She was the youngest Canadian paddler when *Abreast In A Boat* held its 10 Years Celebration in 2005. As such, she carried the Canadian flag at the Opening Ceremonies. Sadly, she died after a courageous battle with cancer at age 39.

Sheila and I gained so much being involved with so many people over the 17 years we operated the booth. What a joy it was to see our 'goslings' laughing, singing, paddling, chatting, making good friends and enjoying this magical adventure that changed their lives. Their families thanked us too.

A CINDERELLA MOMENT

Pat Brown - *Dragons Abreast Toronto 2001* and still paddling

Most of us know the story of Cinderella, where a young woman's faith in miracles got her to the ball that changed her life. This is a special Cinderella story about twenty-two members of *Dragons Abreast Toronto*, members who were fortunate enough to compete in the 4th IDBF World Dragon Boat Racing Championships in Philadelphia in August 2001.

That was my first year paddling, and normally, 'newbies' do not go on international trips. A couple of experienced paddlers were unable to attend at the last minute, so the call went out. My friend Bernie and I couldn't get enough of paddling and were the first to answer that call.

There were approximately 2,500 athletes from over fifty countries participating in the WDBRC that year. *Dragons Abreast Toronto* was one of the teams entered in the Breast Cancer Survivor Race, a charity event to raise awareness about breast cancer. The team was very proud to win the Silver Medal, but we did not take our medal and go home. We competed in the Women's Open Races. *Dragons Abreast Toronto* won the Silver Medal in the North American Club Crew Championships through an incredible team effort, sheer determination, unlimited faith, and a touch of miracle!

A GoodWill Ambassador volunteer at the races, a retired gentleman named Ken made friends with *Dragons Abreast Toronto* members. Ken seemed to derive as much pleasure and pride from our winning as our crew. After winning the second silver medal, Ken ran over, his face flushed with excitement. 'You've heard the story of Cinderella haven't you?' he blurted out. Then Ken went on to say, 'you know you are my Cinderella Team, here you are, a group of women who thought you were going to a party, and you actually ended up at the ball!'

Through the belief of our families, friends, coaches, and especially the faith in ourselves, we made the dream of Cinderella become a reality. It was my honour and privilege to have my heartbeat as one with my fellow *Dragons Abreast Toronto* teammates that first year, as it continues to do 20 years later every time I get in the boat.

AUSTRALIA'S 1ST BREAST CANCER SURVIVOR SWEEP

Elspeth Humphries, *Dragons Abreast ACT*

After completing my treatment for breast cancer in 1999, I travelled back to my native Canada. Newspaper reports of breast cancer dragon boat teams captured my imagination as I had spent many summers on canoe trips in Northern Ontario and eventually in the wilderness of the Northwest Territories (where I met my Australian husband.)

On my return to Canberra, I discovered that an inaugural team was being started by Anna Wellings Booth, sharing the vision of Michelle Hanton. Our first paddlers quickly learned with great enthusiasm from coaches at *Dragon Boat ACT,* but we needed to organise a sweep every time we went out. We wanted to be independent, and I could see that sweeping involved skills I already had.

In a canoe, the stern paddler uses a slightly different stroke to the bow paddler, to steer – it is called the J stroke and allows the canoe to glide smoothly through the water without switching sides. My Canadian camp also had two war canoes that carried 15 pairs of paddlers and a stern paddler to steer and to give instructions - I always loved sterning that huge canoe and the challenge of a perfect landing at the dock.

Our coach, Les Williams, agreed to train me for accreditation. The sweep is in charge of the boat for safety, paddling instructions and often for coaching. It was the beginning of *Dragons Abreast* crews being independent in their own boats. Our dragon spirit and camaraderie thrived through shared stories, laughter and a few tears as we explored our Canberra lake. This is what drew new members to join, become strong with other survivors, and feel whole again.

The skills of steering the boat, deciding the route, going through safety rules, and landing the boat, are just the beginning of what a sweep does with a breast cancer crew. Women come to try dragon boating with aspirations and trepidation. They want to try something new,

something physical, paddling with a group of women who have also had breast cancer and are supportive of each other. They also may feel unsure about this new experience and lack confidence in their physical skills while still recovering from cancer treatment. The women need to feel very welcome, and there must be time for socialising as well as learning the skills of paddling and managing the boat.

This is not a sports team training for competition. Learning to paddle as a team requires technique, building strength, and having fun. Technique develops through clear instructions on the stroke and the movement of the body with the paddle, with demonstrations from competent paddlers. A variety of drills helps the team paddle in time, concentrating and counting the beat of the stroke together. Building strength requires effort, pulling a little harder, reaching a little longer, understanding how your muscles and body work, and what your limits are. Having fun means celebrating achievement, laughing a lot, finding new friendships, and loving every moment on the water. There are pauses to admire the beauty around the boat and think how lucky we are to be out there.

I learned as a sweep to have an awareness of the whole boat; how it was travelling, how to improve our paddling, and to be tuned in to the individual women. I also learned how to encourage them to do their best and enjoy this adventure as part of a team, always remembering why we paddle together and celebrating the pink lady spirit in the dragon boat.

2001 was my first Chinese New Year Regatta on Darling Harbour, Sydney - so colourful, so vibrant. Sweeping was really scary - if you did not pull up in time at the end of the race you were heading for a concrete wall!

In 2005, *Abreast In A Boat* celebrated their 10th anniversary in Vancouver. The regatta was held at False Creek, a very busy waterway at any time of day. Sweeps encountered many occupational hazards and learned quickly to politely give way to bigger boats! I swept for several Australian crews and also for *Pink Butterfly* - my limited Italian now includes some race commands!

New Zealand organised a Pan Pacific regatta in Auckland, and that harbour had really big ships to tangle with. The race start was a concrete wall; sweeps had to back up to it and place the oar on top of the wall. It was nerve-wracking but also exhilarating.

The IBCPC Festival in Peterborough, Ontario, 2010, was a special regatta for me, close to the northern lakes where I paddled so many Canadian summers—one of my camp friends was sweeping for her team too—it was a bit strange to be representing Australia!

Paddling and sweeping with *Dragons Abreast* took me to beautiful waterways - rivers, lakes and dams around Australia. One of the most unusual sweeping experiences for me was taking the helm with *Dragons Abreast NT* to go through the lock at Cullen Bay out to the Arafura Sea.

But perhaps my favourite times were in the translucent light of early morning on Lake Burley Griffin in Canberra, standing at the back of our boat GoAnna, watching the steady rhythm of the paddles and the silver wake behind us. Sometimes we would shout a chorus of the Mammogram Song, and sometimes, we would pause for a Salutation to the Dawn. This was our time in our dragon boat, and we were survivors —pink ladies.

SALUTATION TO THE DAWN

Look to this day
For it is life,
The very life of life.
In its brief course lie all
The realities and verities of existence,
The bliss of growth,
The splendour of action,

The glory of power.
For yesterday is but a dream,
And tomorrow is only a vision.
But today, well lived,
Makes every yesterday a dream of happiness
And every tomorrow a vision of hope.
Look well, therefore, to this day.

-      Sanskrit Proverb

BABY DRAGON - 10 foot tall and bulletproof

Martine Boughton-Paterson, *Dragons Abreast Australia*

I was 24 years old, and it was 1999. I had just been diagnosed, and as I was 10 feet tall, bulletproof, with virtually no support to guide me, I decided to take the risk of a lumpectomy, giving chemo and radiation a large berth. I was just married, completing my second Masters, and we were looking to start a family with a couple of miscarriages already under our belts.

I was offered a referral to Canteen for Kids for support with the cancer diagnosis, but having been presenting to the group's young-uns as a psychologist, I felt too 'old' for this group with the cut off being 24 years old… The other avenue was local support groups, but as a newly married 24-year-old, I felt too 'young' for 'those' support groups…

Up at the local shops I ran into Anna Wellings Booth, who had been the principal's assistant, at my high school, St Francis Xavier College. Excitedly, she shared news of the amazing physical and psycho-social benefits of paddling that a Canadian Doctor had documented. She was recruiting to get a boat on the water in Canberra.

How could I resist? On the water? Fab bunch of gals? Keeping fit? Quasi-support from gals in the know? And we will be catching up for coffee AND cake afterwards?? Where do I sign up?!

A year later I moved to Newcastle NSW, sad to leave my gals behind on the water… But before I could unpack, I received a call from Newcastle 'local' / USA expat Melba Mensch. She lured me to her place with offerings of coffee, cake, and perhaps setting up a group in Newcastle. Word had it a group of rowing club enthusiasts were holding a public meeting– about getting a Dragon Boat Club together, led by the formidable Lynn Flannagan. We invited ourselves to the meeting as virtual professionals in the sport. Melba and I had booked ourselves a flight to Darwin to meet with the Founder of *Dragons Abreast Australia*, Michelle Hanton and get our paddles wet!

The collective bargaining of the pink movement is strong—we offered this to the newly formed *Newcastle Dragon Boat Club*, who had no money and no boat.

Within weeks, Caroline Ahearn (another survivor we had lured in) had negotiated with The Newcastle Port Authority to donate $2,500 for two second-hand boats from Sydney.

But how would we transport them? Where would we keep them? Who was going to fix up the leaky holes? Newcastle Rowing Club came to the rescue. Myself gingerly trying to learn how to sweep— before training and accreditation could stop us from paddling out on the open water in Newcastle Harbour.

We recruited keen women from breast cancer support groups, from specialist doctors, pharmacies. Wherever a woman with breast cancer may go, we were there with a brochure, smile, and promises of cake and coffee after a spin out on the water.

Newcastle hosted the Australian Masters' Games 2001. Dragon boating was one of the sports. As you had to be 27 years old to compete, I took to the microphone to compare. I essentially launched my career in sports commentating, which I am still active in some 20 years, specialising in women's and water sports.

I was fortunate to be offered training in media by BCNA, acting as a Media Representative for both BCNA and *Dragons Abreast Australia*. Again, this was the hatchling for my media career. I am forever grateful for this privilege, the opportunities and doors it has opened for me over the years.

We were finally able to have that baby, and in fact, we went overboard and had a few more. Whilst I stepped out of the boat to have the kiddies, my heart was never too far from *Dragons Abreast*. I still invited myself to their events and fundraisers.

I found it more and more challenging to be a part of *Dragons Abreast* as my close friends passed with recurrences and new cancers. I began to feel like a ticking time bomb.

I memorialised my good friend Dele's memory (President of *Dragons Abreast Newcastle*) in my son's and daughter's names. It broke my heart when she passed away in 2008. In her sad passing, I realised the strength of *Dragons Abreast* and the bonds that we shared. This growing group of crusaders was a beautiful support group not replicated anywhere.

In April of 2019, I was to celebrate 20 years cancer-free. However, I never got to blow up the balloons or pop that champagne. My yearly routine scans and mammograms showed three new cancers which had sprouted in just a year. I was devastated, shattered for our children and my husband. It turns out I am NOT 10 feet tall, nor am I bulletproof. I would have to have that mastectomy and all that treatment I had so deftly avoided.

I haggled my way through the treatment and surgery; it caused me to be severely unwell and irritated other health issues. I had a small window between surgeries and treatment where I could still swim. I decided my last hurrah swim would be a tribute to *Dragons Abreast* in Newcastle Harbour—where I used to take those giggling girls out and tried so hard to stay on the back of that boat as sweep. I was terrified of the sharks known to lurk, getting my ears infected with the polluted water, or getting run over by a coal tanker.

Doing what anyone who still would like to be 10 foot tall and bulletproof looking down the barrel of breast cancer treatment would do—I swam across one of the busiest and largest working harbours escorted by Stockton Beach lifeguards who batted off the sharks and tankers. With my best friend since the beginnings of *Dragons Abreast*, Caroline Ahearn, by my side we raised money (or if you like - bets that a bull shark would spit me out) for my old buddies at *Dragons Abreast* who had been there for me through thick and thin. And now again as a 44-year-old.

It was a triumphant day. Bittersweet as I swam for the last time before breast cancer would take from me again physically. The love and support from the sidelines by those who were there for me in so many ways over the past 20 plus years fuelling my swim.

I thank Anna Wellings Booth every day for literally saving my life with *Dragons Abreast* and the friendships made.

Go Anna xx Paddles Up xx

THAMES DIAMOND JUBILEE PAGEANT, LONDON, UK

On 3 June 2012, four breast cancer paddler dragon boats were privileged to be included in the flotilla down the Thames to mark the Diamond Jubilee of HM Queen Elizabeth II. *Internationally Abreast, Paddlers for Life, Worcester Busters* and, in red & white with the maple leaf, *Abreast from the West.*

Before the event, in the spirit of outreach, *Paddlers for Life, Worcester Busters* and *Internationally Abreast* attended a meeting held at Canada House with the British Breast Cancer Association that focuses on the benefits of physical activity after diagnosis.

Louisa Balderson of *Paddlers for Life* shares, 'We were lucky enough to harness great teamwork, with the backing of Jane (Frost), Jenny (Yule), Dr Don (McKenzie, no less) and many others, who provided support, recruited pink paddlers from around the world and staged a terrific Traditional Afternoon Tea at Canada House, Trafalgar Square, London.'

Eleanor, Founder of *Dragons Abreast Toronto* and co-founder of *Internationally Abreast* was honoured to be part of the *Internationally Abreast 2012* crew which included 5 Canadians, 4 Australians, 3 Americans, 1 New Zealander, 1 South African, 1 Italian, and 1 from Ireland. '*Paddlers for Life* loaned us our boat. Lucy at Low Wood decorated it for us, drove it to London and home again, and in many other ways made it possible to complete this dream, (not the least of which was transporting dry bags of clothes on Sunday so we could change after coming off the water!)'

Jo Parry of *Dragons Abreast Brisbane* shared, 'After the team and supporters met for the first time we had one training session together before the event. It was interesting getting used to each other's different techniques, calls and practising our 'Hip Hip Hoorah' in salute to the Queen.'

Another strong memory for Jo was the British weather, 'When we arrived, London was experiencing a heatwave. That did not last long—the day of the event was cold and rainy. The night before the flotilla, the Australian paddlers were interviewed by the Today Show. It was pouring rain, yet many people were braving the elements to secure their prime position to watch the pageant. Several reports stated that the Thames Diamond Jubilee Pageant was a bigger event than a royal wedding! The atmosphere in London was electric.'

The Thames Barrier was closed to reduce the usually fast-flowing current to 1 knot for Pageant Day, which dawned cool, cloudy and threatening to rain. 'I wore all the shirts I had with me and wished I had remembered my rain pants,' remembers Eleanor. 'We embarked around noon. This entailed carrying the dragon boat down the boat launching area and getting in from the back forward.'

Jo Parry recalls, 'We officially saluted with our 'Hip Hip Hoorah' as we paddled past the Queen's barge. Many rehearsals to make sure we held our paddles up at the right time—not sure we got it right—but pretty certain she did not notice.'

In the late afternoon of 3 June 2012, the Guinness World Records announced that the pageant achieved a new world record for the largest parade of boats.

Paddling a journey of over 15 miles and passing under 14 bridges, Jo remembers, 'Once we reached the Tower of London bridge it was not over for us. The rain and wind increased, and we had another 3 miles to paddle to Greenwich, where we were to disembark. It was soooo very cold. We were grateful to be greeted by our support party with some warm clothes.'

Eleanor shared, 'The finale was going to Canada House on Monday evening, as a team, for a reception of all Canadian participants as they lit a beacon on the roof for the Diamond Jubilee. They had the Canadian Tenors to entertain us and television screens to watch the concert going on up the road.

It was such a privilege to participate in this great event. As the media kept saying, the Brits sure know how to do spectacles. It was a great honour as well to support *Paddlers for Life* as they work to raise awareness of the benefits of physical activity after cancer.'

Louisa Balderson has a vivid recollection of the event 'The River Thames paddle was gruelling. The rain and wind felt like home for *Paddlers for Life*, who come from the far North of England. The unending swell of voices coming from the crowds of people along the river was deafening. Red, white, and blue colours were everywhere, decorating the River Walk and soaring to the sky on apartment balconies. We celebrated our achievement for a long time because we knew 'we'd done OK.'

One thousand boats participated in the flotilla. The opportunity for *Internationally Abreast* to participate was thanks to the exceptional abilities of Jane Frost of *Abreast In A Boat* to pen an application that found favour amidst the 4500 applications received by the selection committee.

THE ACCIDENTAL WEBMASTER

Jan Skorich, *Dragons Abreast Australia*

Eight years after I was diagnosed with breast cancer in 1990, there was no national organisation for breast cancer survivors in Australia. In 1998 we attended a conference in Canberra which saw the beginnings of Breast Cancer Network Australia (BCNA). At that same conference, a photograph of women in a dragon boat in Canada flashed up onto the screen. It caught the imagination of many of us who had never thought we could do something positive around breast cancer. Still, it was Michelle Hanton from the Northern Territory who took the idea forward and launched *Dragons Abreast Australia* (DAA) nationwide. What a vehicle for our breast cancer journey!

In Canberra, Anna Wellings Booth placed a small advertisement in the Canberra Times inviting interested breast cancer survivors to get in a boat and see how we went. I was so excited to be one of those first in the dragon boat.

Dragon boating became a big part of my life; it was always fun and inclusive. We made many friends and spent many hours on the water. It was the first time since my diagnosis to focus on the camaraderie of breast cancer and not dwell on the negatives. In 2000 I was part of the first *Dragons Abreast Australia* team, which participated in Sydney, on the Olympic Rowing Course, no less! We came last, but the crowd was with us!

After participating at countless events, many members travelled to Canada to celebrate the 10th Anniversary of *Abreast In A Boat*. It was there that Australia decided to host the next international festival for breast cancer survivors in Queensland in 2007.

By this time, I had naively offered to become the webmaster for the *Dragons Abreast*. In those days, we needed to write in HTML—no simple templates like we have today. Looking back, it seems strange now that I took on what became an almost full-time job. This was on top of my paid job at the European Union, dragon boat paddling four times a week, as well as the demands of home and family.

Seven of us organised Abreast in Australia 2007—Michelle Hanton, Janelle Gamble, Jo Parry, Anna Wellings Booth, Pete Cardell, and me—with lots of help from families and volunteers.

It was a fantastic experience, both for the 2,000 women who travelled from across the world to participate and for us in Australia. My husband Alek took lots of videos and photos. I particularly remember that he could never get the Italian *Pink Butterfly* team to stand still long enough to get them all in the same shot! Flitting about in all directions, they were so excited—just like the rest of us.

A standout moment was the day of the street parade in Caloundra; we were in the depths of the control room, so busy and engrossed in preparations that we thought we would miss it all. I grabbed Anna, told her to forget about organising buses just for a moment, and we emerged onto the street. We cried together when we saw all those women enjoying the moment, enjoying each other, relishing the sunshine, and just LIVING! Two thousand breast cancer survivors from around the world were showing the positive side of our story. Such energy. Such enthusiasm. Sadness too for friends and family lost to this disease.

Dragons Abreast Canberra survives to this day thanks to the energy and hard work of those still involved. Along the way, we have been part of an academic study that confirmed the benefits of exercise for cancer survivors, a far cry from the days when I was told to take it easy, not lift my arm above my head, or carry my young children.

We are still working towards a world with no breast cancer, but long live *Dragons Abreast Australia* until that day comes!

BECOMING A WARRIOR

Julie Beard

I married an Aussie from Manly, New South Wales in September 2001 and moved to Australia in the months that followed. I came home for Christmas in 2002, had a physical and mammogram, only to discover in January 2003, I had breast cancer. Shocked by this news, my husband encouraged me to stay in the States where my support system was located, and the familiarity of my surroundings would provide me peace and he would go back to Australia to work.

After three lumpectomies, a partial mastectomy and then a full mastectomy, my husband was at a loss as to how to support me emotionally. Attending breast cancer survivor group meetings was not working. Going around the room each week and introducing yourself and telling your experience provided me with a state of sadness that I was struggling to overcome. Each week he would ring to hear my stories about my meeting. We both agreed that this was not a path that was benefiting me.

My husband met an incredible woman, by the name of Michelle Hanton, at a fundraiser in the Northern Territory and soon got involved in being a guest speaker at a breast cancer awareness event. Not long after this meeting, I received an email from my husband with a plane ticket attached to Vancouver, Canada. I assumed that he had

scheduled a holiday for us both but soon realized that this was a solo trip for me and me alone. I had never travelled to another country solo, and I was petrified.

Why in the world was my husband sending me to Canada to meet up with "the Ladies of Port Lincoln" and participate in a Dragon Boat race? I had no clue where Port Lincoln was located in Australia or what a Dragon Boat race entailed.

After many tears and encouragement from my husband, I boarded the plane and arrived in Vancouver. The Ladies from Port Lincoln had yet to arrive; I patiently waited for them in the lobby. With no picture of what these ladies looked like, how would I know who I was meeting? My husband merely laughed.

The Ladies of Port Lincoln arrived, clad in pink, happy go lucky attitudes with smiles as big as the sunshine on all of their faces. All greeted me, hugged me, welcomed me and made me feel like one of "them". I was, in a way, "one of them" in that I was a survivor. I was a "Warrior" (which is what my husband would say). We would share stories into the night about our breast cancer journey. The constant theme that I heard from these incredible women was "support", "team", "love", and "dragon".

I watched as these ladies participated in the Dragon Boat races the following days. Cheering them on, I felt that I belonged to something special. I felt special. I felt like maybe I could become the Warrior that my husband constantly declared that I was. I was then surprised with a consolation race and allowed to participate. I immediately gave an excuse not to participate, as that was my M.O., but these ladies encouraged me to join in and give it a shot. What did I have to lose?

I joined in, listened to the instructions, could feel my heartbeat pounding and then heard the beat of the drum. The cadence was measured in such a way that you picked it up quickly. You could feel the energy from these wonderful ladies in the boat. You could feel energy from all the boats. The same incredible smiles on all of these ladies faces told the story—the story of conquering¬—of pulling together to provide encouragement, strength, and courage. Whether we won the race or not (I honestly do not remember), the inclusiveness, strength, and lift in my self-esteem were the greatest prize of all.

Being a part of the celebration with these incredible women helped me become the Warrior that my husband, Stephen, knew that I was.

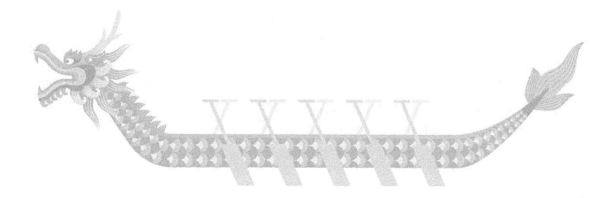

BECOMING A FLORENCE DRAGON LADY

Luisa Moradei, *Florence Dragon Lady*, Founding Member

I'd read in a flyer from LILT announcing they were forming a breast cancer dragon boat team, explaining that paddling was supposed to help with rehabilitation after breast surgery and inviting interested women to participate in a test at a rowing club.

I didn't know what the dragon boat was. Still, the idea of carrying out a team activity, for me accustomed to doing individual sports and now reduced to enforced rest, represented a glimpse into life and being able to count on the strength of other women appealed greatly.

I showed up full of excited expectations and was immediately disappointed because I'd gone to the wrong place. The rowers knew nothing about the initiative but told me there was another rowing club and perhaps the meeting was there. I rushed there on my bicycle, fearful of not arriving in time, but I was lucky.

I found a small group of cold and hesitant women on the bank of the Arno river; they were moving paddles in the air with uncoordinated and clumsy gestures. With a quick indication of how to paddle—I did not understand anything—I kept waving the paddle like a windmill.

After a few brief explanations, we were invited to step into the dragon boat. It was a challenge to get on that long and narrow boat that wobbled as soon as you put your foot down. The fear of falling into the icy February water was so real that for a moment, I regretted having turned up.

The terror and panic vanished by magic as soon as I exchanged silent smiles with the other women, as we each busily tried not to hit each other with the paddles. Within a very short time we were all wet. The water was freezing, and nothing was visible amid the splashes and continuous clash of paddles against each other. But the boat magically moved and was heading towards the city's heart, which we had never seen from the water perspective before.

As the Ponte Vecchio and the whole series of Florentine bridges loomed in the distance, I felt like I was living a dream; it was like opening up again to beauty and life. I discovered the joy of sharing at that moment, and I was firmly aware that the dragon boat would offer me unrepeatable experiences.

Every training session was exciting, and every time I got on the boat, it was like receiving a regenerating injection of confidence and stimulus. Gradually we learned to control our movements, to master the boat and thanks to each of our modest contributions, we were transformed into collective strength. Little by little, we made progress, but above all, we made friends with each other.

At the end of April, we learned from the team in Rome (our godmothers) that the first Breast Cancer Dragon Boat World Championships were being held in September. In Singapore and we were invited!

What to do? We had only two months of training behind us. *Pink Butterfly*, who had already participated in the Vancouver festival, were now a solid team. We were inexperienced and afraid that by joining them, we would hold them back from effectively competing. With affection, they made us understand that the important thing was to participate and be together. They were so convincing that three of us got involved in this adventure and signed up to go to Singapore.

At the end of May each year, the Vogalonga takes place in Venice. A dream for us, aware we had not the slightest chance to participate; we knew that *Pink Butterfly* from Rome would take part—we decided to go and support them.

We set out in a group of five, intent on following these gorgeous women from the edge of the canal. Every time we saw them pass, our hearts swelled, we shouted encouraging phrases at the top of our voices. We felt part of their boat. When they passed under the Rialto Bridge, I was really very excited; they were visibly exhausted. I would have liked to be able to relieve their fatigue. Unfortunately, I could not even scream the encouragement they deserved, 'Come on, come on, you are great' because I had no voice left.

For the first time, outside of experiences within my family, I felt what it really was, in a metaphorical sense, to be one, to set aside a part of oneself to identify with and let live something new that comes from many individuals. At that moment, as I stood on the edge of a canal watching them paddle, I had a surreal experience. Having noted the great show of strength demonstrated by the *Pink Butterfly* made each of us more aware of their message. It lifted our admiration and created a bond of love with our founding team: 'If they can do it, we can do it too'.

With practice and determination, we gradually improved. Simultaneously, creating a relationship of affection and friendship between women of different ages and experiences within the team. This was an equally important benefit of the exercise.

DON'T WONDER WHAT IF?

An inspiring snapshot of Jenny Petterson, Dragons Abreast Australia

Jenny and Joanne Petterson were identical twins in every way. Sunny smiles, always willing to help, great athletes...the one difference between them was Jenny had breast cancer. It was through her diagnosis that Jenny found paddling. With her twin sister Joanne, as a paddling supporter, they became members of *Dragons Abreast Sydney*.

Paddling gave Jenny a chance to be like everyone else, and she loved the training, competing and being part of a team.

Always thinking of others and willing to share her story to inspire and support others on the breast cancer journey, Jenny became a speaker for the Breast Cancer Network of Australia (BCNA) and the National Breast Cancer Foundation (NBCF). She finished every speech with suggestions that helped her through her 12-year journey living life with cancer:

1. Keep a positive attitude

2. Live each day one at a time but do set goals for yourself

3. Surround yourself with positive, supportive people

4. Take time for yourself, and

5. Do something with your life that you really enjoy.

Jenny really enjoyed dragon boating. The dragon spirit guided her paddling career to the highest levels on the competitive world stage, but she never forgot her roots with the breast cancer movement.

Her husband, Geoff Eldridge, takes up the story. 'We were married three years after Jenny's diagnosis. She had 11 tumours in her lungs at that stage; the wedding was organised in 3 months as we weren't sure how long she had. We were lucky to be married for almost 10 years.

The 2009 IDBF World Championships were to be held in Racice in the northern Czech Republic. All three of us had made the Senior A Australian Team via a successful State-vs-State campaign at the 2009 AusDBF Championships held at Kawana/Qld in late April 2009.

Jenny had raced with the prognosis that there was little more that could be done via conventional treatments for someone who had lived with cancer for 12 years. Her cancer had metastasized to the liver for the second time, and she was experiencing migraines. Despite this, Jenny was a fighter, determined and competed for NSW and her sports club, *Pacific Dragons* at the Australia National Titles.

In early May, we trialled individually to confirm our places in the Australian Senior A Team for Racice. Barely a week later, Jenny's nagging migraines were diagnosed as a 4cm brain tumour on the left side of her brain. Reluctantly she withdrew from the squad.

Jo and I trained on, awaiting the course of Jenny's treatment. Initially, the brain tumour would be removed. Then, the liver tumours would be managed by internal radiation [Selective Internal Radiation Therapy using SIR-Spheres]. The following week the brain tumour was removed during a four-hour operation. In the next week, specialists helped her to learn to walk and speak again. The day before she was to come home, her heart failed.

The last week in ICU was incredibly difficult. We communicated with Jenny with our words and gestures. We were holding her hand, massaging her feet and reading extracts from her favourite books. Photos from all our adventures were pinned to the walls. She was surrounded by care and love. Many staff knew Jenny from her 12 years of treatments, she was always positive, and the hospital staff loved her. Sadly, we lost Jenny on Tuesday, 30 June, 2009.

Jo and I decided to go to Racice with Jenny in our hearts and minds. It's what she would have wanted us to do. I concluded my eulogy to Jenny, 'she will guide and inspire us from above'.

It was hard, but we were back in the boat the day after Jenny's funeral. A week later, we were time trialling, and with personal best efforts, cementing our place in the Mixed Senior A Team.

At the last team trial before departing to compete in Racice, the Australian Squad presented Jo and me with a gift in Jenny's Memory. It was a star, located in the southern sky, in the Constellation of Vela named in the memory of Jenny Petterson.

Vela is Latin for Sail. The star was picked because of the Constellation's water-themed name. Jo and I view the star from the Sydney Observatory each year on their birthday.

Jenny participated in an inspiring book project titled 'A Pocketful of Sequins', short words of comfort, wisdom and inspiration from breast cancer sufferers, families and supporters. Jenny's contribution 'Step outside your comfort zone. Give it a try. Don't wonder what if?'.

At this presentation, each member of the Australian squad was presented with a green, gold and blue wristband with Jenny's name and 'Don't wonder what if?' inscribed.

At this stage, Jo and I were training on instinct and for relief. We were there but not there. Numb in the loss and feeling the pain of the void in our lives. The water was the only place to find some escape from the emotional loss, turmoil and pain we were experiencing.

On Friday, 28 August 2009, a dream would come true for the Australian 500m Mixed Senior A team. We paddled beyond ourselves that day to cross the final line first for the Gold Medal, wearing our inscribed wristbands dedicated to Jenny.

We felt no pain. We did what we trained to, responded to every call and 'made the impossible, possible' as the Germans told us. It was a special time in Australian Dragon Boat history; everyone there that day will always remember the moment.

A day later, Mike Haslam, President of the IDBF, sought out Jo and me amongst the competitors and crowds to present us with a special gold medal for Jenny. A few tears were shed as we talked about Jenny, our lives and the difficult days ahead. Mike had always been a supporter of the breast cancer survivor movement in dragon boating.

Jenny and Jo first met Mike in Berlin in 2005 as part of *Internationally Abreast*. Every subsequent international dragon boat event had seen them reconnected. Each meeting finished with a photo of Jenny, Mike and Jo, taken by me. In parting in 2009, we finished with the usual picture; this time, I took Jenny's spot with Jo holding Jenny's paddle adorned with the special gold medal from Mike.

Jo and I continue to paddle with Jenny as our guiding light and inspiration. Jenny's gift to us of paddling has helped us through the hard times and allowed us to lead our lives with purpose.

Paddling has been a constant in our lives, and the irony is that we would not have found it if Jenny had not had breast cancer. Jenny would often say, 'what would we be doing if we did not start paddling?'. We feel we are better people because of our paddling experiences - there is always a silver lining'.

THE NITTY GRITTY OF RESEARCH

Susan Harris (aka Top Hand Sue), *Abreast In A Boat*

As the resident academic 'geek' on *Abreast In A Boat,* I decided to morph our initial foray onto False Creek in 1996 into a bona fide research project. With the capable assistance of Dr. Sherri Magee (nee Niesen-Vertommen) – a PhD student at the time and one of our three coaches, we set out to test the hypothesis that vigorous, repetitive upper extremity exercise would not lead to lymphedema in the affected arm.

According to the prestigious journal of the US National Cancer Institute, three strategies for preventing lymphedema were: (1) use the affected arm in moderation; (2) do not carry heavy objects; and (3) avoid repetitive upper extremity motion. Dragon Boat racing certainly flies in the face of preventive measures #1 and #3!

Using a case series methodology, we measured the arm circumferences of 20 of the 24 original members at three time points: (1) at the beginning of paddling training (baseline); (2) at the end of the race season 2 months later; and (3) 5-6 months after the end of the race season. All of these women (ages 31 – 63) were at high risk for developing lymphedema, i.e., all had received Level I-II axillary dissection with an average of 12.9 lymph nodes removed and about two-thirds had also received breast and/or axillary radiation. Both are significant risk factors for developing lymphedema.

We defined clinically significant lymphedema as a difference between the involved and uninvolved arms of >1.0 inch at the final measurement session. None of the women demonstrated clinically significant differences at any of the four landmarks measured on each arm. We concluded that: 'Results of our series of case reports suggest that women who have received axillary dissection and, in many cases radiation, for the treatment of breast cancer can safely engage in strenuous upper extremity exercise without incurring lymphedema.' Our caveat however was: 'This is a testable hypothesis that must be answered definitively through a prospective, well-controlled trial.

Future research in this area could serve to further enhance the quality of life of women living with breast cancer.'

Since that study was published in 2000 – the first of its kind to 'throw water' on the longstanding myths about risks for developing lymphedema – it has been cited 103 times, not only by authors of more methodologically stringent studies that lent further support to our tentative hypothesis but also by the Canadian clinical practice guidelines on breast-cancer related lymphedema, the New England Journal of Medicine, the Journal of Clinical Oncology, and other cancer journals. In a 2020 review article on the history of exercise and lymphedema, Harris, Niesen-Vertommen and Dr Don McKenzie were referred to as 'pioneers' in this field!

As a result of Dr McKenzie's groundbreaking 'experiment' on False Creek in 1996 and the 2000 study published by Harris and Niesen-Vertommen, there are now over 250 breast cancer dragon boat teams around the world in over 32 different countries, suggesting thousands of breast cancer survivors are encountering the same joie de vivre that we as the *Originals* were lucky enough to experience more than a quarter-century ago!

REFERENCES

Erickson VS, Pearson ML, Ganz PA, et al. Arm edema in breast cancer patients. Journal of the National Cancer Institute. 2001;93:96-111.

Harris SR, Niesen-Vertommen SL. Challenging the myth of exercise-induced lymphedema in breast cancer: a series of case reports. Journal of Surgical Oncology. 2000;74:95-99.

Johansson K, Hayes S. A historical account of the role of exercise in the prevention and treatment of cancer-related lymphedema. Lymphology. 2020;53:55-62.

McKenzie DC. Abreast in a boat--a race against breast cancer. Canadian Medical Association Journal. 1998;159(4):376-378.

THE LAST WORD

Jane Frost, *Abreast In A Boat, Original, 1997 - Present*

'Never doubt that a small group of committed, dedicated individuals can change the world; indeed, it is the only thing that ever has.' Margaret Mead

Abreast In A Boat was a small group of twenty-four spirited, brave and fit women who, by crossing the finish line at the Alcan Festival in Vancouver, Canada, in 1996, launched a Canadian legend and an international movement. I feel as passionate about it today as I did those 25 years ago when we got into the boat for the first time.

I remember our first race. It was 650 metres. I thought I was going to die. Recently, Esther, one of my fellow *Original* paddlers, told me about that race; halfway down the course, she said to herself: 'This is my first race, and it will be my last.' She is still paddling today.

And then there is Dr Don McKenzie, aided and abetted by his two colleagues, Diana Jespersen and Sherri Niesen Magee. Little did Don know he would become a 'rockstar' for breast cancer paddlers. He continues to support and encourage us, and he does much more behind the scenes. He has been the Canadian medical coach for our Olympic flatwater paddlers for over 30 years. He spearheads the Canadian Anti-Doping Program. He has given 'Exercise is Medicine' presentations to many of the international sports organizations. Practically every week, he fields calls from paddlers and medical personnel.

In 2001, Don was awarded the Meritorious Service Medal for his work with *Abreast In A Boat*. The citation ended with these words: 'His remarkable achievements, enhanced by his guidance and caring, have given breast cancer survivors across Canada a sense of confidence and pride, and a lifeline to a better existence.' Don is and always has been about the paddlers, never himself.

I recall reading an article on the motivation of dragon boat paddlers. The article explained there are two kinds of motivation: intrinsic, motivated by internal things and extrinsic, motivated by external things. The author went on to say that some paddlers are in it for the glory and the medals. Those are my words, not hers, and others are in it for themselves and their teammates; to make them stronger, fitter paddlers and to contribute as a team member. Each has its own rewards.

When we hold our festivals, they are participatory and inclusive, deliberately inclusive of all different fitness levels. We paddle not just for ourselves but also for those watching us from the shore, who we hope are thinking, 'if they can do it, so can I.'

To my fellow paddlers, I salute you. You, too, have changed the world. You are living examples of life after breast cancer. Our collective responsibility as those fortunate enough to be survivors is to spread our message far and wide; there is life after breast cancer—a life filled with laughter, joy, and fitness.

Our collective challenge is continuing this movement into the future, to reach those less fortunate and in countries less developed.

Paddling has been one of the great joys of my life. It has given me the priceless gift of friendships, much laughter, love, and support. And here are the lessons I learned that first year and by which I live even more every day, for I am blessed to be a person living with breast cancer.

To dig our paddles deep

To keep our gaze clear

To laugh a lot and out loud

To celebrate our lives

To mourn our losses

To work to find the cause of this disease, and

To know we are making a difference.

I have an important message to those newly diagnosed or recently out of treatment: there is a full and active life for you despite breast cancer. You are not alone; you do not have to stay home. It takes some energy to start training but the benefits far outweigh the effort. By becoming a breast cancer paddler, you will not dwell on your diagnosis. You will regain control of your life. Your family and friends will be comforted and encouraged when they see you paddling your heart out, racing for the finish line and celebrating your life with a group of people who know where you have been.

We urge you to join us. Paddles Up. Go Gently.

ABREAST IN A BOAT TEAM SONG

'Beautiful Paddling Weather' was written by Tim King, also a cancer survivor.

Beautiful paddling weather

We're out on the water again.

We paddle ourselves to exhaustion

In the sun and the wind and the rain.

So we all pull together

'Cause that's what will keep us afloat

To raise breast cancer awareness

That's why we're *Abreast in a Boat*.

We've all seen rough water

With waves that have pounded our bow

We've paddled straight up over mountains

Nothing can stop us now

As we all pull together

'Cause that's what will keep us float

Our spirit will never be conquered

'Cause we are *Abreast in a Boat*.

Paddling's become our new challenge

And life is quite dif-fer-ent now

But it's funny we'd never have met you

If those waves hadn't pounded our bow.

So we're happy to paddle together

On an ocean or river or lake

Our message of hope is increasing

And we're proud of the difference we make.

ADDITIONAL READING

Challenging the myth of exercise-induced lymphedema following breast cancer: a series of case reports, S R Harris, S L Niesen-Vertommen, Journal of Surgical Oncology 2000;74:95-99

Living Life to the Limits: Dragon Boaters and Breast Cancer, Terry Mitchell and Eleanor Nielsen, Canadian Woman Studies, Vol. 21, Number 3:50-57

Exercise Adherence in Breast Cancer Survivors Training for a Dragon Boat Race…., Kerry S. Courneya, Chris M.Blanchard, Dot M. Laing, Psycho-Oncology 10:444-452.

Picking Up the Pieces; Moving Forward After Surviving Cancer

Sherri Magee, Ph. D. and Kathy Scalzo, M. S. O. D.

Raincoast Books, Vancouver, Canada, 2006

How to Ride A Dragon: Women with Breast Cancer Tell Their Stories

Michelle Tocher, www.Lulu.com

A Dragons' Tale

Anna Wellings Booth and Michelle Hanton, Dragons Abreast Australia

Are You Ready? Attention! Go!

Die ladybugs – im drachenboot gegen den brustkrebs

Heike Auel, Ventura Verlag, Germany

ABOUT THE AUTHORS

Eleanor Nielsen, diagnosed with breast cancer in 1989 at 51, underwent a mastectomy and chemotherapy. Retiring as National Director of Programs for the Canadian Cancer Society in 1991, she became the founder of *Dragons Abreast Toronto* in 1997.

Eleanor guided the publication of How to Ride a Dragon: 22 women with breast cancer tell their stories, written by Michelle Tocher, now in its second edition print.

In 2004 Eleanor started the Ontario (now Central Canada) Breast Cancer Dragon Boat Network. She was honoured with the Governor-General's Caring Canadian Award in 2009.

Eleanor can be found gardening, hiking, and enjoying time with her husband, Charles, and their combined family of five couples and six grandchildren when not paddling.

Michelle Hanton was diagnosed with breast cancer in 1997 at age 38.

Michelle became a breast cancer advocate through the Advocacy & Science Training run by the National Health & Medical Research Council.

She is the founder of Dragons Abreast Australia, Inaugural Executive President of the International Breast Cancer Paddlers Commission (IBCPC). Michelle is a founding member of NT Breast Cancer Voice, a former State Representative for Breast Cancer Network Australia, and has served on the National Breast Cancer Foundation Consumer Advisory Panel.

Awarded the Order of Australia in 2008 for her contribution to women's health, Michelle was in 2010 the first female to be awarded Life Membership of the Australian Dragon Boat Federation.

GLOSSARY

First in our lane - Lane placing is not of importance because breast cancer survivors who are able to paddle consider themselves winners because we are able to participate.

Pink Ladies - breast cancer survivors

Paddles Up - raise your paddles ready start paddling

Take It Away - start to paddle

Brace the Boat, Staybilize, Feather - put your paddles flat on the water

Vinaka Vakalevu - thank you in Fijian

Bula - Welcome in Fijian

ACRONYMS

AIAB - Abreast In A Boat

AusDBF - Australian Dragon Boat Federation

BCS - Breast Cancer Survivor

BCNA - Breast Cancer Network Australia

DAA - Dragons Abreast Australia

EDBF - European Dragon Boat Federation

NBCF - National Breast Cancer Foundation

IBCPC - International Breast Cancer Paddlers Commission

IDBF - International Dragon Boat Federation

IPPC - International Pink Paddlers Commission

ACKNOWLEDGEMENTS

We wish to thank the following individuals who provided information, support, and guidance to bring this book to publication.

Kim Bonomo

Charles A Dixon

Jane Frost

Doug Graydon

Akky Mansikka

Mary McAvoy

Caroline McTomney

Cecilia Picchi

Joanne Preece

Judy Smith

Betty Solley

Jenny Yule

JOIN OUR COMMUNITY

https://www.facebook.com/InternationallyAbreast

Never underestimate the impact of the breast cancer paddlers 25 years since the movement began. Several teams started because someone first saw or heard of a breast cancer team at an event.

Inspiration. Hope. Courage.

Printed in Australia
AUHW021500271021
354375AU00048B/308

9 780645 288902